Family Roots

A Mother's Search for Meaning

Family Roots
A Mother's Search for Meaning

Marian Shannon Miller Lord
with Larry Lord

Deeds Publishing | Atlanta

Published by Deeds Publishing in Athens, GA
www.deedspublishing.com

Printed in The United States of America

Cover photograph by Myrtie Cope Photography ©

Text layout by Mark Babcock

Library of Congress Cataloging-in-Publications data is available upon request.

ISBN 978-1-947309-05-0

Books are available in quantity for promotional or premium use. For information, email info@deedspublishing.com.

First Edition, 2017

10 9 8 7 6 5 4 3 2 1

In memory of my mother, Marian Shannon Ross Miller,
who gave me her name and half my genes

Prologue

One fall day in 1982, when I was thirty-six, I sat folded in a small oak kindergarten chair across from my son's teacher at a school conference. I had my legs in place, my blonde ponytail in best Grace Kelly fashion, as someone had once described it, and my Southern good manners to attention at the table where I was assigned. Nevertheless, I strained to hear the mother of twin boys as she spoke to the other teacher across the room. "My boys have finished reading my husband's old Hardy Boys mysteries. What would you suggest they read next?"

She had to be kidding.

Her twins, along with Hunter — our towheaded six-year old son — and several other children with summer birthdays were beginning a second year of kindergarten, although at our house we euphemistically called it *pre-first*. I had convinced my husband Larry that it was prudent to hold Hunter back to give him that extra advantage, a new educational trend at the time.

As the Hardy Boys conversation wafted my way, the teacher at my table spoke. "Mrs. Lord, I'm glad to have an opportunity to talk. You see: We can tell Hunter is smart and remembers most everything we say in class, but we're concerned about him. He doesn't relate well to his classmates in a typical way. Some of his actions aren't developmentally delayed, they're simply *inappropriate*. Also, he's having great difficulty learning to read. I can't quite put my finger on it; Hunter is somehow — well — different from other children. I've talked to the director of the pre-school, and we encourage you to have him tested — both psychologically *and* neurologically."

I do not remember the rest of the conference with this teacher. But I do recall shedding my calm persona as I ran to my car. In my frozen hands, I clutched a piece of paper with names of doctors the teacher had recommended. Out of breath, I pushed wisps of hair away from my face. I gripped the steering wheel and sat staring, trying to catch my breath. I felt like crying, but I couldn't.

How could this be? How did this happen? Why my son? My family?

As the teacher's comments reverberated, flashes of my own childhood, siblings, and parents flew through my mind. Both sides of my family had been strong pioneers in our country, and highly successful in academics and careers. I could not reconcile the teacher's concerns with my own history and our expectations for our first-born son.

The search for answers would take seven frustrating years of visits to experts in medicine, psychology, and education, and many false leads and dead-end paths. It also required scrutinizing my family roots and history and finally facing and solving a painful — yet long denied — family mystery.

PART I

Discovery

1. My Roots and Early Years

My story is deeply rooted in the Hunter clan, which, according to family legend, were the official hunters for the Scottish King David I in 1116. Almost 900 years ago, William the Hunter was appointed as Royal Huntsman Praefectus Venatorus Regis to the Kings and Queens of Scotland while his wife had the honor of serving Queen *Matilda* as lady-in-waiting. They had been granted land in Ayrshire, on the coast west of Glasgow, where for generations they lived and hunted with cross-bows made from an ancient yew tree that still grows on the property. But as the centuries went by, some of the clan became restless and decided to seek fame and fortune in America.

In the mid-1880's my great grandparents, Robert and Marian Shannon Hunter, set sail from Scotland with two small children to seek business opportunities in America. They had no idea what kind of weather, sickness, or other hardships would befall them or how long the trip would take. Obviously, they were risk takers. Their destination was Darien, Georgia, where Robert's brother James had already developed a booming timber export business.

Subsequently, in the late 1880's after the southern longleaf yellow pine forests in that area had been harvested, the two brothers and their families moved to Mobile, Alabama to establish a similar operation, taking advantage of the large, natural harbor of Mobile Bay, which was also abundant with virgin timber forests. They built sawmills along the Alabama and Tombigbee Rivers that fed into the bay. Within two years they employed over 500 people to cut trees and load the finest of them through a hole into the bowels of sailing ships that made close to 200 trips to Europe in a year. Despite their ancient lineage and royal connections and their current economic success, the Hunters initially were not part of the establishment in Mobile. According to one cousin, the old Mobile families regarded the Hunters as "nothing but carpetbaggers, only they didn't come from the North!"

The Hunters eventually had eight children, including my grandmother, Mary Hunter, one of their four daughters. Sadly, she died at age forty when my mother and her younger sister were five and three. Having heard about three different causes of death from as many relatives, to this day, I still don't know why she died so young.

The Hunter family grew and thrived in Mobile. In the 1950s, my mother's first cousin, another Marian and a well-known local artist, drew the Hunter family tree as a gift to each young Hunter relative who got married. Ours hung in our house as a subliminal reminder of one large branch of my heritage. My great grand-mother's name, Marian Shannon, for whom my mother and I were named, is inscribed at the base of the tree with her forebears among the roots. The names Marian and Shannon are sprinkled generously throughout the tree, revealing that, through the generations, our Hunter clan has shown little imagination in naming our female offspring.

In contrast to many contemporary families whose members are dispersed across the country, large numbers of six generations of Hunters have stayed in the Mobile-Fairhope area. Many of the Hunters and their descendants have been and remain important players in business, community affairs, and the arts. They are also members of the mystic societies, secret social groups that organize and present floats and balls during the annual Mobile Mardi Gras Carnival. Family members have often participated as members of the royal court. Old newspapers and photo albums show the adults attired in their ball gowns or the pastel suits as they played the roles of equerries and pages of the king and queen's court. The Mobile Carnival is a tiered, caste driven affair, and the Hunters, despite being viewed as carpet baggers in the late nineteenth century, became an integral part of upper echelons of Mobile society.

I've often wondered *why* so many Hunters have remained in the Mobile area. Is it because of abiding devotion to family and familiarity? Or is it the lure of the bay, gulf, and rivers for fishing and recreation? fine woodlands and open fields for deer, quail and turkey hunting? or the mild winters? or an unwillingness or inability to adapt to change?

My paternal grandfather, Patrick Henry Miller (his family modestly acknowledged being direct descendants of the patriot), had been a gentleman farmer in Arkansas. When he became president of a cooperage company in Mobile, he moved there with his family. My father started second grade soon after they arrived and attended a private boys' school. Even though the fam-

ily has lived in Mobile since the early 1920s, old Mobilians forever considered the Millers *newcomers*. Thus, my father did not
grow up in the same tier of Mobile society as my mother and her
Hunter family did. Nevertheless, he firmly believed in the values
and manners of Southern gentility and expected all his children
to live up to them.

Despite our strong family roots in Mobile, I did not spend all
my childhood in this rarified atmosphere. My father was in the
U. S. Navy, and, by the time he retired when I was fourteen, we
had moved nine times and I had attended eight different schools.
My childhood is neatly pigeon-holed into the places we lived,
each with its own story, shape, duration, tone, and texture in the
overall bird's-eye view of my life. In each place, I made friends
and good grades. From my childhood perspective at the time,
that was simply what my three brothers and I did. It was our
family responsibility. Inevitably, there had been some challenges,
but I remember feeling mostly happy and successful; my siblings
and I always took school and social life in stride.

Everywhere we lived, we found other military children eager
for friends, and we had the run of the Navy bases. At dusk on
summer nights, we played touch football and sardines (a hide-
and-seek game where you hide in pairs until you are found), and
kick-the-can; we could walk to the Olympic-sized pool or ride
the Navy bus to the movies. We always lived near the water and
that provided a vague continuity of place, despite our frequent
moves. In the process of all the moves, my brothers and I became
independent, self-reliant, and adaptable, but it was never easy
leaving friends and familiar surroundings.

As long as I can remember, I tried to balance the societal expectations of a young dutiful Southern daughter with my intense yearning for adventure. Good manners and appropriate behavior had been inculcated into all aspects of my childhood. "Yes, ma'am"; "No, sir"; "Please"; and "Thank you" were an indelible part of my lexicon. The dinner table was highly regulated, especially when my father was at home. Left hands stayed in our laps when we weren't using our knife. We learned that you always serve food on the left, take dishes away from the right. I heard the story of a woman hired for the first time to assist with a dinner party. Upon arrival, she asked the lady of the house, "Does you *stack*, or does you *tote*?" At our house, we were *never* allowed to stack.

Ironically, my father, who strictly enforced these rules, also encouraged me to take risks and test myself. I never felt as emotionally close to my father as I did to my mother but appreciate that he was an accomplished man, a practical realist, and a highly skilled engineer. He could build almost anything, including our beach house. He created enterprises like our crab farm on Weeks Bay. He involved all his children in his projects, and, as a result, solving problems, satisfying curiosity, organizing, inventing, building, and repairing things came naturally to all five of us. I owe any ingenuity I have to my father. Woven into learning these skills were messages to do our best with integrity and to complete what we start. We were a family of doers.

My father also shared his love of sports with us. When he was younger, his performance on the track and football fields earned him a place in his school's hall of fame, and he encouraged us to participate in athletics. Two of my brothers and I swam competitively. All five of us participated in a variety of other sports that included football, baseball, soccer, or golf. Even though I was a girl, he expected me to be able to learn a wide range of athletic and practical skills.

"C'mon, Shannon," he said one Saturday. "I want to teach you how to throw a football. You throw like a girl; here—put your fingers on the laces like this ..."

And I learned to throw a perfect spiral.

Emotionally I was much closer to my mother, but this connection often conflicted with my efforts to assert my independence. One day while we were living in Honolulu and before I was old enough to go to school, my mother dozed off during naptime and assumed that I was doing likewise. But wide-awake and dressed in my green and white muumuu just like hers, I sneaked out the back door to visit a neighbor, even though I knew I was not supposed to leave the house. A few minutes later, knowing I had a narrow window of time, as I hurriedly climbed back over the fence I snagged and tore my muumuu. How would I explain the rip? I could not think of an alibi or excuse and reluctantly told her the truth. My mother scolded me, enough so that I never did it again, but, at the same time, she made me feel proud that I ventured away and had the courage to confess.

Another day, also during naptime, I cut a wide lock of my bangs and hid the hair and scissors under the bed so no one would know! My mother was no fool, but she did not make a big deal out of it; my hair would grow back. Then, too, there were those times when I played doctor in the greenhouse in our backyard with neighborhood children. I knew my mother would not approve, but I never got caught and never revealed those adventures. In addition, there were fights with my brothers, some of which I probably instigated but flatly denied my role. My mother wisely chose her battles, and we all survived.

My mother was truly a devoted and tender parent. She greeted us every afternoon after school, always wanting to be there for us. She once told me, "If there was something bothering any of you, it would spill out the minute you walked in."

Her homespun but sage advice to me was often, "Ask other people about themselves. That's what they want to talk about." Long after my mother's death, her sister told me that my mother understood human nature better than anyone else she had ever known. Regardless of what we did at home, within the everyday workings of the family, my mother always marveled at our accomplishments, many of which she was not able or inclined to attempt. I always felt that she loved and believed in each one of us; and I always hoped that someday I'd be like her as a mother.

At the same time, I sensed on some basic level that my mother needed me to *support* her, not act against her. Around age four or five I remember hearing my mother more than once tell a new friend, "When Shannon was born, I had my nuh-vus..." I wondered why her lead-in was always, "When Shannon was born..." I assumed I must have caused this thing to happen, and, although I didn't know exactly what it was, I could tell by the tone of her voice that it wasn't good. A few years later I gathered that "nuh-vus" was a euphemism cloaked in my mother's southern accent for a nervous breakdown, or some undesirable mental state less severe than a full-blown breakdown. Whatever the case, early on I determined that I must do everything I could to prevent this dreadful thing from happening again. Although at the time I was unable to verbalize my thoughts, I somehow sensed in her a fragility that needed my support.

I now understand why Momma had whatever she had. My father was stationed in Norfolk, Virginia shortly after World War II and had to be away with his squadron several days every week. As wife of a naval officer and total stranger in this post-war town, my mother was twenty-four and seven months pregnant with me. She already had two sons who were two and three-and-a-half. After I was born, she would lay awake worrying about how, when Daddy was away, she could get three babies out of the house in case of fire.

A life-long friend who came from New York to help with her nuh-vus once told me, "She would lie on the couch and say, 'Feel my heart! Feel my heart!'" No doubt it was palpitating because of her perpetual state of anxiety. Or, was there something more to the story? But Momma survived, and went on to have a third son three years later and a daughter ten years after that.

As I reflect on my childhood, I realize that I, too, was often anxious and, if the truth be known, I was more of a pleaser—sometimes at a cost to myself—than a risk-taker. I had two older brothers, one head-strong and adventurous, the other more artistic, inward, and compliant. I aimed for the middle; I took *some* risks but got caught often enough to learn that disobeying rules would result in unpleasant consequences. So, despite my desire for adventure and my father's encouragement to test myself, I more often than not chose to err on the side of caution.

School work came easy to me, but in second grade I made my first "B". My father's question spoke volumes about him. "Why did you make a 'B' in science?" to which I replied in this pre-Sputnik Russian satellite era, before science was emphasized in the curriculum, "What's *science*?"

Even though I truly didn't know what *science* was when I was seven, over the next few years I absorbed the expectation that I would attend college as naturally as the oxygen that sustained me. After all, my father and his siblings had graduated from college in the 1930's; my father went to the Naval Academy, one uncle to law school and the other to medical school; my aunt also completed college. Although my mother did not graduate, she attended the University of Alabama. In 1900, her father had graduated from the University of Alabama, followed by many family members in the years to come.

When my father retired from the Navy, my parents chose to return to Mobile, where they both had grown up, and where so many Hunters and other relatives were deeply rooted, much like the Spanish-moss-laden live oaks whose branches arch over the main thoroughfare of Mobile. My three brothers and I, like our parents, viewed this move as *going home again* since we had visited many times and had lived there when my father was away on a ship for a year. It was a dramatic homecoming for my mother after living all over the country and leading a very different life from what she had known in her youth. My father also was facing many changes as he retired from a job in which he had flown propeller and jet engine aircraft, fought in England and Africa during World War II, flown wounded soldiers from Korea to Honolulu during the Korean War, and planned the Atlantic Ocean recovery of the first manned space-satellite capsule. Yet, shortly after our arrival at my aunt's house, the conversation quickly turned to ho-hum, local talk: "Which bank was better, the Merchants or the First National?"

Soon we bought and settled into our very own two-story house—nicer than our usual Navy issue—just before my ninth-grade year. As in every other place we had lived, I listened intently to my new friends and adapted my accent to fit in. I met classmates whose parents had grown up with mine and people of all ages who were related to me. I began to feel that, perhaps like the Hunters and other branches of my family, I truly *belonged in this place*—a short filament in a large and intricately spun web. I was intrigued that so many people knew more about my family and where I fit in than I did. "Why, you must be William Buck Ross's granddaughter—or Miss Pud's niece—or Uncle Doc's double second cousin once removed..."

Happily, my social life was not limited to my extended family, and I had many friends and dates. Classmates, sons of my parents' acquaintances, and friends of my brothers invited me out. Some were older than me by several years, which bothered my mother, but, as always, she trusted me to do the right thing. A few of these young men continued to be in touch after I went to college, but I was always cautious about getting too involved.

After high school, I followed my family's academic expectations and went to Bennett College, a beautiful all women's college, nestled in the rolling hills north of New York City. I studied art history, French, and English. It was during the 1960s, a time of many social changes; and it was my real awakening to the ways of the world. Many of my classmates were girls from generations of young women from prominent American families who had attended Bennett over its 90-year history. I was probably considered privileged, but I learned that there were levels of wealth that far exceeded my own. Bennett offered me the chance to broaden my mind and experience in other ways as well. For example, on one excursion to New York City, we spent the day with Benny Andrews, a nationally renowned African American artist (1930-2006) whose work depicted social injustices and the suffering of many groups as part of his ongoing project to explore and understand what it means to be American. My learning continued apace.

After an enlightening experience at Bennett, I returned to Mobile to continue my education at University of South Alabama and received a Bachelor of Arts degree in 1968. Finally, I had the opportunity to explore the world and consider who I was and how I would venture into this new broader arena of freedom.

As I contemplated my future, I felt torn between being a traditional Southern lady and mother and a world-wide adventurer. This conflict had always been part of my life but was sparked anew when I heard Betty Friedan give a lecture at Bennett. As the product of parents — actually, several generations — steeped in the conservatism and established gender roles of the Deep South, I was incredulous at Friedan's message: motherhood would not be enough unless all women were seen as capable as men and as comparable partners in their endeavors. Women need not, she seemed to say, fritter away their lives.

I had grown up immersed (as many of the first crop of Baby Boomers still were) in a very different message: my ideal role would be staying home and helping to shape my children's lives — letting go of their chubby little hands as they took their first steps; bandaging their skinned knees and kissing them when they fell; cheering them on at their first T-ball games; supporting them in school; serving as room mother, team mother, and chauffeur. In short, I was trying to give them the best life had to offer. Those expectations were all I knew, and they defined my future. The women's movement challenged these assumptions, but at the time, I did not realize I could get loans for graduate school. Thus, I trained for a profession.

Yet in my own way, I did resist those traditional expectations and, after college, traveled and struck out on own for a while. My first adventure was working as an au-pair in Switzerland for a summer. I had put an ad in the New York Times stating that I wanted a summer job in Europe. My mother did not understand why I wanted to do that kind of work, when we had household help at home. After all, she had married at age twenty, had her first baby at twenty-one and probably never entertained such yearnings. It was impossible for me to explain to her what I wanted to do.

This experience made me aware of the intricacies and illusions of family life at a whole new level. I worked for a family with three children, ages 3 to 10. The parents and their guests had values which were quite different from what I had learned as a child. Lawrence, one of the guests, bore an amazing resemblance to the youngest child. I wondered but never inquired about the coincidence. Another guest, an Israeli biologist, decided to stay home one day while the others went boating. While I was making the bed in his room, he appeared and pressed his amorous intentions. Fortunately, I was strong enough to physically resist him, but came away with a whole new understanding about the undercurrents of family life and the ways people treat each other.

When I returned to Mobile, I applied and was accepted as an airline reservationist with Delta Air Lines in New Orleans, which offered me more opportunities to travel. I moved to this exciting city with great expectations, although I spent my days diligently working in a large windowless room. It was a challenging job because we had to treat every customer as "the most important passenger who ever booked with Delta." Fortunately, I had the determination and personality to deal with even the most difficult ticket seekers. Working for Delta gave me the opportunity to travel—but only on short trips. I longed to spend more time in a new place much as I had in Switzerland but definitely not as an au pair.

I had studied French in high school and it had improved while I was in Switzerland. I figured an immersion experience would help me to become fluent. N'est–ce pas? Paris was my choice, and I was thrilled to be accepted into a 3-month course at the Alliance Française in Paris that included living with a French family. The French classes were exciting as I learned to speak, read, write, and … conjugate! The only downside of the adventure was living with the French family. They had three children, and I shared a bathroom with them. Toward the end, I got tired of living in such close quarters and always having to talk to someone … in French! I was ready for this adventure to end and longed to be back home. As soon as the program ended, I bought my ticket and headed home.

Upon returning to Mobile, I began searching for a job, but I was picky—I did not want just any job, and after a short time, I decided to move to Atlanta where several of my high school friends lived. My father was disappointed in my decision, but in August of 1970, I packed up everything in my Volkswagen station wagon and headed to Atlanta, unsure of what lay in store for me. A few weeks later, I received an offer to teach school in Mobile, and my father called me and tried to persuade me to come back and take the job. He pointed out, "It's a bird in the hand!" And I said, "I'm not coming back." At that moment, I made a break from my family and the expectations and constraints of life in the upper echelons of Mobile society.

I moved in with my friend Beverly who offered me a room in the basement of the house that she shared with two other women. I was thrilled to be on my own but somewhat apprehensive about finding employment, which I needed to fund my new life. After a few days, I was offered a job at a bookstore for $1.27 an hour. Even though it was a poverty level wage, I took it so I could have some income.

Soon after arriving, I began to make new friends, and I met Tom, a lawyer in Atlanta. We started going out right away on a frequent basis. I am not sure if my motivation was self-preservation, entertainment, or hopes for a long-term relationship, but it was a way to get out and do more than I could on my minimum wage.

Soon after I arrived, Beverly had a group of college friends coming for the weekend, and she ask me if I would stay with another Mobile friend named Leslie. While I was there, a young man named Larry Lord came to pick up Leslie for a date to go to the Georgia Tech football game. Larry was from Mobile, and I had briefly dated his younger brother Wayne. When Larry arrived, I opened the door. I said, "You must be Wayne's brother." We talked for a few minutes, and then Larry and Leslie left. Unbeknownst to me, after taking Leslie home, he called his step-mother in Mobile and asked if she could get my phone number from my mom.

Although Larry had grown up in Mobile, his family's background was different from mine. The Lord family had lived in the Crawford community outside Mobile for several generations. Larry's grandfather owned a farm that included a large pecan orchard and acres of vegetables and melons. Larry's father, Herron, worked on the family farm as a youngster and sold watermelons and pumpkins in a nearby town. However, he was ambitions and always wanted to do more with his life. He was the first graduate of Semmes High School. After his graduation, he moved into Mobile and joined his brother who had started a tire business. Larry's mother, Kay Thompson, also grew up in Mobile. Her family was comfortable and well-connected but not part of the upper echelon that the Hunter family occupied. Herron and Kay married in 1938, and in 1942 Larry was born.

Larry and I started dating, but I did not totally dismiss Tom, and I enjoyed going out almost every weekend night. In the fall of that year, Jon, an old flame of mine who lived in Jackson Hole, Wyoming, came to visit me. One day Larry called to make plans for the weekend, as was his regular routine, but, because of Jon's visit, I told him I was busy for at least the next week. Larry, who was not sure what this meant, came by the bookstore later that day to find out what was going on. I was not sure what I wanted at that point so I told him, "I'm pretty busy right now, I will call you." The reprise with Jon was short lived, and after a couple of weeks, I called Larry and our dating resumed.

Larry was determined and embarked on an energetic courtship. As we got to know each other, we realized that we shared many values. Education was important in his family, as in mine. He had attended the same private boys' school where my father, uncles, grandfather, and brothers had gone. He had completed the five-year professional architecture program at Georgia Tech; his only brother, Wayne, had earned a Doctor of Philosophy in History, and his mother had graduated from the University of Alabama. I learned that he had managed to survive one of the most profound losses imaginable to a child; when he was eight his mother died of ovarian cancer.

After I had known Larry quite a while, he began to reveal some of his life experiences about his mother. He shared the story of the first birthday party he attended after she died. Just as his friend's mother arrived to give him a ride to the party, he remembered he was supposed to take a present, and his father had forgotten to get one. He ran to his piggy bank and shook out as many coins as he could, quickly put them in an envelope, and gave it to the mother of the birthday boy. "I didn't know what to get Win, so I brought him some money to buy what he wanted." Larry later recalled there was probably about eighty-nine cents in the envelope. But the point is that, when caught in a bind, he thought of *something to do* to rectify the situation. Despite the terrible loss, he had learned how to survive and solve problems. I admired his resilience.

With his optimism and determination, Larry flourished. In high school, he was a member of the National Honor Society and a member and officer of a high school fraternity. At Georgia Tech, he was president of the Student AIA (American Institute of Architects) Chapter. He served as a company commander in Vietnam and was chosen from thirty officers in his Navy Sea-bee Battalion in Vietnam to galvanize a team of twelve men to go into the Mekong Delta to rebuild Vietnamese villages. Larry is unfailingly optimistic; his glass is not simply *half-full*; it is perpetually *overflowing* with his *can-do* attitude. He seems to be powered by a relentless motor that seldom stalls or sputters, and he is rarely depressed or angry.

Larry's enthusiasm always has included athletics. Although rarely making first string, he threw himself into the sports he loved with his usual verve—baseball, football, basketball, and tennis; as a child, he spent many nights dribbling and practicing free throws in his back yard until dark.

Larry and I are different but complement each other in many ways. He has indomitable energy that never fades, whereas I have to muster my energy. From the first, I liked his sensibilities, his love of music, and his visual appreciation of the world through architecture and photography. Plain and simple, I liked that he *loved* what he did at work and play. And we shared similar values of family, integrity, and hard work. Less than a month after Jon came and went, Larry asked me to marry him. After thinking about it for a couple of days, I accepted. We were married on August 21, 1971, at the Episcopal Church in Mobile that my family had attended for decades. Our wedding was a traditional southern affair with an abundance of family and friends in attendance and close friends in the wedding party. It was a hot and humid day in August, and we were relieved to be taken to the airport and make our way to St. John's in the Virgin Island for our honeymoon.

I was 26 years old and ready to give up some of my former independence and move to an interdependent phase of life. Larry had also had many world-wide adventures and at 29 was ready to settle in one place and build his career as an architect. We were both excited about starting a family and believed that we were aligned for a perfect life together.

The following year, we realized that we could benefit from some additional income so I went to Georgia State to get my teaching certificate. The following year, I got a job teaching French and English at Wheeler High School. I found that teaching five courses with about 25 students each was overwhelming for me. Preparing for classes and grading papers depleted all my energy and spare time.

The kids offered me more new perspectives on life, as I saw for the first time the reality and effects of drug use. Over the year, I came to realize that certain students were stoned most, if not all, of the time. But I was still shocked when, toward the end of the year, a young student gave me a wadded-up piece of paper that contained some brown crumpled leaves and a note saying, "I don't know if you smoke, but if you do, here is some really good stuff!" I decided I could not continue teaching and maintain my sanity. At the end of the school year, I collected my small pension and started to think about what I would do next.

Earlier I had been asked to join the Junior League of Atlanta, which requires involvement in the community. To fulfill my service, I volunteered at the Tullie Smith House, a restored mid-19th Century farm house and outbuildings that were part of the Atlanta History Center. I enjoyed working there and was delighted when they offered me a job as docent coordinator. I organized a lot of activities for kids, including an annual petting zoo when a lot of animals were brought to the farm. During one of these events, a pig got loose and hid under a corn crib, and I called Larry to come help us out. While he was grabbing the pig and getting it out, the pig rent the air with deafening squeals. These experiences made me realize that I did love to teach, and that, for me, the Tullie Smith House was a much more relaxed and joyful place to engage children in learning than a high school classroom.

One of the activities we conducted at the Tullie Smith House was cooking in the separate kitchen building, the inside of which was stained with soot from the open fire. As we gained more experience in fireplace cooking, a couple of other volunteers and I decided we should create a cookbook. We embarked on that task and titled the cookbook—before we had written a line: "Tullie's Receipts." We did a lot of research and collected many traditional recipes, household hints, remedies, and general wisdom from earlier centuries (e.g., natural dyeing of textiles, using weights and measures). As we explored several sources, we came across the name of Clifford Shillinglaw, a chemist and former Head of Technical Operations at Coca-Cola.

Dr. Shillinglaw lived in New York City and was a collector of historical cookbooks, but his fame came from the fact that he was one of two men who knew the secret of the Coca-Cola formula and was responsible for mixing syrup for the bottlers. We went to meet with him to discuss our plans for a cookbook. Visiting New York City with three other women from Atlanta proved interesting, and we had many adventures and learned a lot. One of our group who had a very distinctive Southern drawl tried to befriend the person operating the newspaper kiosk just outside the door of our hotel. The first day she was rebuffed; the second day there was a brief conversation; the third day a very long conversation ensued; and on our last day, the little man started waving and talking before we could even initiate conversation ourselves.

Looking back, I can see that as a child and young adult, I often vacillated between the traditional expectations for well-bred Southern women and the lure of adventure, travel, and accomplishment in the wider world. My job at the Tullie House allowed me to embrace both aspirations. I was immersed in Southern history and traditions yet had opportunities to explore my other side — from chasing squealing pigs, to traveling to New York, to creating a cookbook. Larry was always supportive of my plans and ideas so, although I was married, I still had a lot of independence and could choose and follow my own path in many ways. However, as Larry and I started to think about having a family, I knew that many things would change.

2. Hunter

In the process of deciding to have children, I realized that I was caught between two worlds, time periods, and role expectations for women. I hearkened back to Betty Friedan's speech that I had heard in college and thought about the feminist push for women to have careers. After much deliberation, my upbringing and my mother's stay-at-home example and advice tipped the scales. Larry and I determined that, although we might have to make hard choices at times, we could live on his architect's salary. While it might be the same trap that Friedan called the *feminine mystique*, I had been taught that motherhood was happiness, and I was not worried about staying home. Underneath these ruminations about whether or not to stay home, *I somehow knew I did not have the physical stamina and emotional fortitude to juggle children and career at the same time.*

Throughout these deliberations, I never doubted that we would be good parents. After all, I had spent countless hours caring for my baby sister Katie, thirteen years my junior. I recalled one Saturday before Christmas, my mother went Christmas shopping and asked me to baby-sit for Katie, then eleven months old and very mobile but not quite walking. While my mother was gone, I cut out a jumper and blouse I was making as a Christmas present. All the while, Katie was tangling herself in thread, and constantly pulling up on my stool. But I kept her safe and nearly completed the jumper and blouse by the end of the day. In short, I arrived at motherhood feeling quite confident about child-rearing and the attendant responsibilities.

We also assumed that, with our shared values and inheritance, and the role-modeling that we would provide, our children would be academically successful, go to college, harness their talents, become independent, and make a contribution to the world, small or large. It was never *if* they went to college and became successful; it was simply a question of *where and how*. And we were confident we would live long enough to see our grandchildren do the same.

However, our journey was far from the smooth road that we had imagined.

First, we struggled with infertility. After two years of marriage, we started to seek help. For several months, Larry and I conscientiously charted my daily temperature with a basal thermometer. Larry had had his sperm count tested earlier and was told, "You're a *blue-ribbon winner!*" It was clear that the problem was mine. My menstrual periods had always been irregular so there was no predictable way to determine when or if I would ovulate. We had tried without intervention for over two years to have a child. Finally, shortly after starting the fertility drug clomid, I became pregnant; at last, I was going to be a mother! Although a little tired at times, I mostly felt great, and the months passed smoothly.

I have sometimes wondered what would have happened if I had *not* taken fertility drugs and had accepted my fate without children and gone about my life. Would I have found some other gratifying purpose? Was my body trying to tell me something? Does modern science sometimes allow us to push beyond optimal limits? However, Larry and I desperately longed for a child. It seemed as if a seed of yearning had been planted by a knowing gardener in us along with millions of other young couples to ensure the perpetuation of mankind; or, to satisfy a longing to leave a legacy; or, simply to bring someone into the world to love. Whatever the case, we longed to have a baby and were willing to utilize modern methods to make it happen.

Having attended a Lamaze course with me, Larry was prepared to assist during labor. He wore a birthing-coach T-shirt created by a colleague and sported a whistle around his neck. As our teacher suggested, he carried lollipops, peppermint sticks, and other birthing necessities and humorously stored them in a small yellow and green bag resembling a Crayola box. He threw himself into the impending birth with the same gusto he exuded in everything he did. I didn't find much humor in his antics but didn't say much. I assumed his actions were a cover for the overwhelming sense of the unknown, the fear, excitement, and anticipation of his soon to be realized responsibility as a father.

I started labor at seven one morning. With contractions increasing through the morning, I convinced Larry it was time. After a midday trip to the doctor, we were sent home; and, as I would have expected, Larry returned to the office and after work played in his weekly softball game behind a church. We did not have Blackberries or iPhones in those days, but Larry was concerned enough to sprint to the church office to call me after every inning. "Y' okay? — *My bat!* Call ya later!"

Arriving home at 10 PM and exhausted, Larry was asleep before his head hit the pillow. My labor pains were growing more intense and closer together. And my coach had taken himself out of the game.

"*Wake up!*" I yelled after a couple of contractions. "*Big help you are!*"

Larry's birthing props quickly lost their luster and became downright annoying as my labor dragged on excruciatingly through the night. Finally, we drove to the hospital around 4 AM.

Our Lamaze teacher had emphatically proclaimed several times that contractions are *pressure — not pain.* As we confidently went through this course, Larry and I were determined not to use any anesthetics, including an epidural. Now I wondered with every contraction, *whom* did she think she was kidding? The *fathers?* Yet we remained firm in our determination to avoid pain medication.

After sitting with me through twenty-seven hours of labor and missing a night's sleep, Larry went to breakfast. While he was gone, I called in the anesthesiologist for an epidural. Entering the room the doctor mumbled, "*You women who think you can do this without any help*" — *a* comment that made me want to kick him. After all, I had made it through a day and night without his assistance.

When Larry returned from breakfast he was a bit annoyed that I had cratered in his absence. The epidural worked but lost its effectiveness after only three hours. Although the anesthesiologist tried, he was unable to give me additional relief. Once again,

I was writhing in exhausted agony. The obstetrician appeared and told me to start pushing, then disappeared again. The baby was posterior rather than the normal face-down position, but I did as I was told and began pushing. The doctor looked in occasionally, surprisingly not more often. Three hours later I was still pushing with tears streaming down my face. Still no baby. I tried different Lamaze breathing techniques. Everything I knew. Nothing helped. I wanted to slip out of my skin and hover above it all. There *had* to be another way. There *had* to be.

Recognizing the ever-increasing danger of the situation with my ebbing strength to push, Larry, in his commanding and now irritated voice, suddenly blurted, *"Get the doctor—quick! She can't make it much longer!"* It was three weeks after my due date. The obstetrician finally came and ordered me moved to the delivery room. At first, he tried unsuccessfully to turn the baby *in utero* with his hands. Again, I yearned desperately to levitate above the process. *Something. Anything.* Nothing had offered relief. *There had to be another way for this baby to be born.*

Larry was such an integral part of this miracle about to happen, yet he was left to look on helplessly as I writhed in pain. After failing to turn the baby with his hands in-utero, the doctor was forced to use forceps. Three pushes later and the head crowned. In minutes, I was holding a nine-pound, two-ounce baby boy with red marks from the forceps delivery on both sides of his face, a very squashed forehead and, later I discovered, the largest head in the nursery. Despite the agony, finally our baby was here.

Late that afternoon, Larry and I celebrated our fifth anniversary by sharing a cold hospital hamburger left from lunch. The next morning a florist delivered a dozen Tropicana roses from one of Larry's colleagues at the office just as his boss appeared with a lovely basket of Champagne and caviar—fitting libations for the previous day's events.

It was 1976 when births were still infused with mystery and surprise about the unborn baby's sex. In true Scottish fashion, Larry and I had chosen family names for both sexes. For a boy, we had decided on *Hunter Thomson Lord*. Larry and I liked the cadence and story behind the name Hunter, my maternal family name. Thomson was the surname of Larry's maternal grandmother. One friend exclaimed, "Poor kid! You gave him two last names and a title!"

We were ecstatic that finally we had a son who was now the center of our universe; and we would spare nothing to assure him a good life. Our hopes and fantasies soared.

One day at a book store, as I carried Hunter in a baby carrier snug against my chest, I spotted a book—*Drama of the Gifted Child*. Glancing down at my precious bundle now peacefully sleeping, and knowing nothing about the book, but somehow *believing* that Hunter was most surely gifted, I glanced hurriedly in two directions before I self-consciously reached for a copy. I eagerly awaited Hunter's afternoon naptime so I could read it, only to learn that the book was about *narcissism*. Still steadfast in my beliefs, I was confident that I needed simply to wait and see his gifts unfold.

With his hair like unblemished corn silk and his eyes as sky-blue as a cloudless day, he was in my eyes the most beautiful child in the world. A friend suggested he become a child model, but we wanted to spare him the pressure of such a pursuit.

As time went on, however, I also noticed that Hunter was,

well, a *little* different from other children. In truth, my uneasiness about Hunter began to fester in early infancy when he didn't hold his head up well at four months. He also did not sit up, crawl, or walk at the normal times mentioned in early childhood books. He never crawled on all fours; he pulled himself on his belly like a Marine in the jungle. I was keenly aware that he always fell at the late end of normal in most of his gross motor skills, but reassured myself that *he was still within the norm.*

Also, as a toddler, his interactions with playmates were often a little odd. He would use body language — pointing, gesturing — when words were called for. "Hunter," I would say, "Please *say* what you mean. We like to hear your pleasant voice." Some of his answers to peers' questions were nonsense words. In his early years, I eagerly anticipated Hunter's weekly playgroup. I dropped him at another house to play with three other toddlers and enjoyed my freedom for a few hours. But every fourth week I dreaded my turn to have the playgroup at *my* house. Invariably he would bite or hit and manage to elicit an outrage from every child. Also, I found hosting the playgroup exhausting and always hoped I would have the stamina to endure the morning. I counted the minutes until the other mothers returned so I could take a nap.

I was finding motherhood far more challenging than I had ever imagined, and nothing quite made sense. Hunter was able to recite several nursery rhymes before he was two, and we thought that quite advanced. Yet, in kindergarten, he struggled to learn to read so we had held him back. And there were times when he would get wound up, then start jumping from one piece of furniture to the next. I felt nervous about leaving him with just any teen-age baby sitter. One day, when he was two, my mother watched him play happily in his sand box for quite a long time. She remarked, "He may enjoy people, but he will also enjoy spending a lot of time alone." I, however, yearned for him to get invited to birthday parties, to occasionally be king of the mountain, to feel comfortable in athletic endeavors and successful in school.

I reassured myself with memories of nightly readings beginning when he was less than a year. Normally he was not a cuddly baby; he would arch his back until I put him down. But when he was tired and ready for bed, he would relax into my lap as we read *Good Night Moon* night after night after night. He could point to the balloon, the telephone, and the bear and kittens when I asked him. As he got older, his favorite book was Richard Scarry's, *Cars and Trucks and Things that Go* that he called the *Gold-Bug Book*. He would point out the tiny gold bug obscurely placed on nearly every page. At these moments, I was living the motherhood I had imagined. Hunter may have been behind in some motor skills, but he was obviously very intelligent.

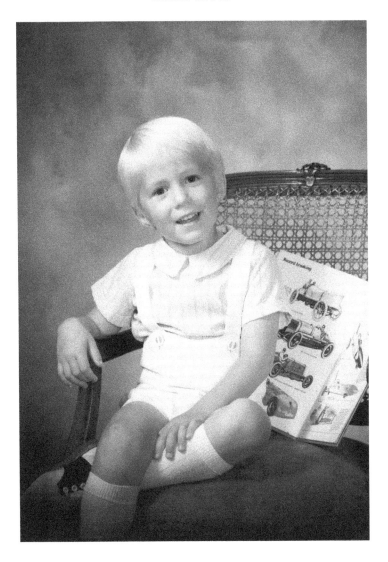

3. Ashby

*Reflecting back, I now understand the significance of my infer-*tility. At the time, however, I was not aware of any implications other than the immediate challenges that we faced. Because I had difficulty conceiving Hunter, I took Clomid to help me get pregnant each time after that. I had a miscarriage in 1979 but kept trying. Two years later, I gave birth to Ashby on July 18, 1981, when Hunter was almost five-years old.

My pregnancy with Ashby was uneventful until a routine glucose-tolerance test revealed high blood sugar, although it was not full-blown gestational diabetes. The day after the due date for Ashby, my contractions began shortly after dinner. Since my labor with Hunter had lasted thirty-six hours, we were in no hurry to leave for the hospital. We leisurely packed up Hunter's things and prepared to drop him at a friend's house.

Having taken a refresher Lamaze course, Larry and I were experienced and prepared this time around and, as my obstetrician said, "You now have a proven pelvis!" But memories of the excruciating birth of Hunter prompted pause. This time, however, I was able to laugh a few times between contractions. Lying on my side, I was watching the screen of the fetal heart monitor when suddenly the pattern on the screen changed. The nurse instructed me to turn the other way. What was going on? Later I learned that Ashby had shown signs of cardiac distress at that moment.

Larry, fully awake and present with no nonsense, unlike the time before, coached my breathing—*he-he-whooo, he-he-whooo.* And shortly after midnight I gave birth to a seven pound ten-ounce baby boy, this time *without* anesthesia. Ashby weighed less than Hunter, had a smaller head and made a far less dramatic entry into the world.

As with Hunter, we gave him family names: Jonathan for Jonathan Buck, my maternal grandfather, whose family came south from Bucksport, Maine, and Ashby for Larry's paternal grandmother, Nina Ashbee.

Over the next few hours, Ashby nursed briefly and then jerked his head away. When the pediatrician arrived, I commented on his nursing pattern and asked why his hands and feet were blue.

"Oh, he's a fine little fellow! I'd keep him if I were you!" he replied, not answering my questions. "Oh," he added, "and his plumbing works just fine!" He pointed to his wet shirt.

A few hours later, a nurse knocked at my door. She informed me that Ashby was having difficulty breathing and had been moved to NICU—the *neo-natal intensive care unit.* She assured me he was stable, the nurses would keep close watch and if his situation got worse they would call in the neo-natologist, a brand-new specialist at this hospital.

I was already feeling breathless, my heart racing, as I grabbed my robe and followed the nurse down the hall. I gasped at the sight of jumbled wires of too many colors to count — red, orange, blue, yellow, green, and more — attached to Ashby's tiny chest as he lay in an incubator under a transparent dome.

Barely sleeping that night, I wrestled among the sheets through long, fitful periods. Why couldn't I take my baby home, tie a helium balloon on the mailbox like most people? Why another traumatic birth?

Then, at 4 AM, there came another knock.

"Mrs. Lord, I'm sorry to disturb you," a gentle male voice whispered.

"Oh, I'm not asleep," I blurted as I bolted upright.

"I'm Leonard Sacks, the new neo-natologist at Piedmont Hospital. I've been called in on your son's case."

My heart nearly leapt out of my throat as I sprang from bed and padded down to NICU, this time alongside Dr. Sacks. "Your son is suffering from *meconium aspirations*. He aspirated a mixture of amniotic fluid and meconium into his lungs before he was born; meconium is a baby's first, very thick, sticky stool, and it is now interfering with his breathing. But with careful observation and treatment — administering oxygen if necessary — I suspect he'll be fine in a few days."

Dr. Sacks' self-assured, gentle manner calmed me, and I was glad that my day-old infant was now in his care. But still, the next few days dragged endlessly, especially the day Larry flew to San Antonio to work on an expansion to the airport there. With red, puffy eyes I travelled the hall often to check on *Tommy Tubes*, as we called Ashby at the time.

Larry's departure prompted many reflections about myself and Larry and our lives together. Did Larry not perceive Ashby's

situation to be as grave and scary as I did? Had I led him to believe that I was so resilient and independent that I was capable of
handling *every* situation by myself? Why didn't I ask him *not* to
go to San Antonio? It was not that he could have done anything
to help Ashby, but his presence gave me strength. Why was I
unable to ask for support, the very thing I needed most? I was
caught in a magnetic field of *dependence* versus *independence* like
the pair of small black and white Scottie dog magnets that I had
as a child. Now Larry's career was soaring, and within the magnetic fields of family and work, he was often pulled toward work.
Did my dilemma stem from my early childhood of not wanting
to impose on my mother—or anyone—and my reluctance to
ask for help?

Amazingly, our health insurance allowed me to stay in the
hospital for the full week that Ashby was there. Because he was
too weak to suckle, like a dutiful cow, I went to the room I dubbed
the dairy to pump milk several times a day. In a few days, when
Ashby's condition improved, I was able to nurse him by carefully
lifting him from the incubator while he was still connected to the
monitors. If a gauge plunged, I had to stop nursing, until it returned to normal. It's a wonder my milk didn't dry up completely.

Hunter, who had been staying at our friends' house, finally got
to see his baby brother on his third visit to the hospital. A nurse
brought him to the viewing window, a thick pane of glass that
separated their worlds. Hunter kept jumping, flapping his arms
and screaming, *"Is that our baby?—Is that our baby?"*

At last, on the seventh day of his life, Ashby was allowed to
go home. The first afternoon, shortly after putting him down for
a nap, I heard a blood-curdling scream. Hunter burst out of Ash-

by's room like a circus clown. *"I didn't pinch his leg! I didn't pinch his leg!"* he shrieked and raced through the house. The next day I heard Ashby again let out a scream, almost a cry of indignation. Again, I ran to Ashby's room to find Hunter holding his baby brother by one leg, dangling him upside down like a butcher inspecting a plucked chicken. Ashby had survived a week in NICU but now had landed on a rocky road in Hunter's territory.

Meanwhile Larry continued working hard on his airport project. Six months after Ashby was born, during an unusually bad snow storm in Atlanta, he managed to catch the last flight out before the airport closed. After a couple of snowed-in days with 5½ year old Hunter whining, pinching his baby brother, and throwing toys into his crib, I felt like jumping ship. Equivocating for a long time, I finally picked up the phone, hesitated, and put it down again. I loathed asking for help from *any*one. Finally, I picked it up again and called my brother-in-law, Wayne, who lived nearby. He had barely managed to make it home in the storm two days before, and his wife had made it only as far as her co-worker's house. He was home alone, and best of all, *willing* to help-out.

A few minutes later, I nudged Hunter toward his first solo trip over the hill and through the leafless woods that separated our two houses. Even though the distance was short, the trek was quite steep, and I nervously watched Hunter, clad in orange jacket and black boots, slipping on the white slopes, falling numerous times, and disappearing over the hill. This time my usual concerns about such a trip were replaced with relief out of sheer desperation to have space between us. But with a first child, how does a parent distinguish between appropriate and needless worry? Whatever the answer, my brother-in-law helped preserve my sanity that cold winter afternoon.

Now, thinking back to my own childhood when my brothers and I were free to roam Navy bases and neighborhoods, I realize that we would have blazed a well-worn path to our uncle's house long before we were five years old. Hunter, in contrast, hovered close to home, never venturing into the woods to explore or go down to the spring to catch tadpoles.

While Hunter was away that snowy day, I made a cup of tea, succumbed to the soothing embrace of an over-stuffed chair and remembered to breathe. Since Ashby was now taking a nap, I dozed off to fortify myself for Hunter's return.

I thought about friends who also had young children, but parenting seemed to drain me more than them. I took naps often, and my emotional underpinnings could be easily knocked from under me. In retrospect, I wonder if I was suffering from Seasonal Affective Disorder (S.A.D.) or post-partum depression. Or was I facing Betty Friedan's "problem that has no name," a woman's unhappiness and dissatisfaction with an idealized image of femininity in her role as housewife and mother? Or was it some combination of the above?

During the period right after Ashby's birth, photos of Hunter show him frowning over the realization that *this baby was here to stay*. They reflected his state of mind and, in some ways, my own sense of powerlessness. But I remember how excited I was about Ashby. He was self-confident from the beginning.

4. Seeking Answers

Before Hunter started school, I was concerned about him, but the conference with his kindergarten teacher that I described in the prologue to this book still came as a shock. It turned out to be a pivotal moment for all of us. After I fled from the school, I sat in the car in the parking lot, our hopes and dreams for Hunter starting to blow away in the biting wind of the teacher's words: "inappropriate," "different," "concerned," and "test him—both psychologically *and* neurologically." But oddly, the next moment I was *almost relieved* that my concerns about Hunter had finally been noticed by someone else. The teacher's words had ripped off the thin veil of denials, exposing the harsh reality that something was wrong. Although I did not realize it at the time, our family had embarked on a new journey—an odyssey as I came to call it—that was unlike anything we had known or expected.

Nights around the kitchen table, Larry and I rehashed the teacher's comments. We recalled moments of Hunter's early years, trying to find clues to what was going on, alternately feeling reassured and concerned. We wondered how all this related to Hunter's angry reaction to Ashby's birth the previous year. A few years earlier we had been elated when Hunter was accepted to an elite private school where we knew he would receive a fine education. Even now our tuition payments were providing dividends with the teacher's astute observations and professional guidance. We hoped that with early intervention we would get him back on track.

We immediately contacted psychologist Melinda Peril who had evaluated many children that we knew. She tested Hunter, and we learned that he had an IQ of 130. We knew he was smart, but he had all these odd behavioral problems and difficulty reading. The psychologist diagnosed him as having ADD and recommended that he go to a school for children with special needs. We were disappointed not to keep him at the prestigious private school, but we quickly accepted the fact that this was the best course of action.

While Hunter was undergoing psychological testing, we asked friends for recommendations for doctors to do the neurological evaluations and finally decided on the internationally renowned pediatric neurologist recommended by the teacher. We had to wait four weeks for the appointment—weeks that seemed to stretch endlessly. When our appointment day with the pediatric neurologist finally arrived, we went, as I had gone to the school conference, feeling grown up and confident, embodying the formality and propriety of our Southern upbringing. Larry, an imposing six-foot five with blond hair thinning on top, was wearing his usual coat and tie. Hunter was carefully dressed in his school clothes and was on his best behavior. As the three of us entered the doctor's office, I stood confident and eager, a mother in quest of answers. But beneath my air of sangfroid, I was awed by the doctor's reputation and hoped that he couldn't see my heart pounding with anxiety and dread. After all, a neurology appointment for *a six-year old* was way beyond what we had expected at this point in Hunter's life.

I didn't know any other children who had been referred to a neurologist. Nor did I know other parents whose conferences with teachers always revealed some concern about their child, like mine had with Hunter's. I naively assumed that my children's young lives would flow as easily as I remembered mine had.

The pediatric neurologist appeared with glasses and slicked-back, wavy brown hair. He offered a hand and cursory greeting, suggested that Larry and I sit down, and then quickly got down to business. He tapped Hunter's knees and other body parts with a black rubber and chrome hammer, watched him walk on heels and toes, tested finger to nose, heel to shin—we assumed the usual exam—then dismissed Hunter to the waiting room.

The doctor closed the door and pivoted toward us. *"Why are you here?"*

I shifted my weight and crossed my legs, cleared my throat and reported the teacher's concerns and the evaluation results from the psychologist. The doctor rolled his eyes.

"*Every*one has *learning* and *attention* problems these days! They're in vogue! So, *what*, may I ask, are you doing about them?" He raised an eyebrow and crossed his arms on his chest.

I glanced at Larry, grabbed the arms of my chair and began to speak. "Well, our pediatrician—who, I'll admit, may be on the fringes if not over the edge—suggested hair analysis and vitamin therapy."

"And *what*, may I ask, is he *low* in?" he smirked, arms now akimbo.

45

Feeling as if he had sucked all the air out of me, I inhaled a couple of times and finally replied, "Selenium and copper."

He rolled his eyes again and thrust his arms in the air.

"If he's low in copper, give him a penny to chew on!"

As if by pneumatic force, an oppressive silence filled the room as we realized we would get no solace nor any answers to our puzzling situation with Hunter. Larry and I once again exchanged glances and eked out a perfunctory thank you as we closed the door behind us. With my hair standing up on my back of my neck and my tail between my legs, Larry and I quickly collected Hunter and left.

Many years after this appointment, we became privy to Hunter's medical records and read this doctor's conclusions that would prove to be so wrong:

> There is no impairment of fine motor coordination, and he cooperated extremely well ... did not demonstrate impulsivity ... demonstrated good understanding of verbal communication ... does not appear to have the characteristics of a learning disability or attention deficit ... not a candidate for stimulant medication ... may have a personality or behavioral problem and would benefit from supervised activities with other children ... placement in a [special] school ... would be entirely inappropriate. I do not believe the child is neurologically impaired. I also do not think the child shows any evidence of vitamin or mineral deficiency, and he is certainly physically and nutritionally adequate.

In the days following the sarcastic response from the neurologist, I reflected on scenes and situations from Hunter's first few years trying to understand what was happening. *Why* was I so determined to know the cause of his challenges? Why not a more *laissez-faire* attitude? I thought about my father always fixing things and making me test myself, such as learning to drive a stick shift car and painting the beach house that he and my brothers were building. Perhaps it was those high expectations and challenges growing up that pushed me to keep on going. Although I felt dejected and furious after the appointment with the neurologist, I did not waver from my determination to find a plausible explanation for Hunter's struggles.

We now had our seatbelts fastened and were speeding up the on-ramp to somewhere, but *where* we still hadn't the vaguest notion. At that point, Larry and I realized that we would need to take charge and manage our children's health issues. We could not leave decisions to the "experts" as the following example demonstrates.

Despite the disparaging comments of the pediatric neurologist, I continued giving Hunter selenium. Four years after the appointment, we were still giving Hunter vitamins and mineral supplements. Running out of selenium one day I decided not to replenish it—just to see if it was doing any good. Was our pediatrician or the neurologist right? Three weeks later, Hunter's teacher called. "Is everything okay at home? Is there anything I need to know? Hunter has not been himself for about three weeks."

I racked my brain. I assured her nothing had changed. Suddenly it dawned on me: Could the selenium have an impact on Hunter's behavior?

Unbeknownst to the teacher, I replenished it and three weeks later checked back.

"He's back to his normal self!" she announced, much relieved.

As this story shows, we often felt confused by conflicting recommendations. One research study concluded one thing, the next study the opposite. One doctor espoused this; the next prescribed that. How and why selenium works is a mystery, but Hunter takes selenium to this day.

Although the neurologist had dismissed our concerns, I knew something was wrong. I trusted his teachers' observations of Hunter and how he compared with twenty other children over a period of months more than the doctor's ten-minute meeting and brief neurologic exam. Besides, the teachers' concerns and psychologists' evaluations had shored up my own observations and intuitions. I knew something was wrong, and I was determined to find out what was causing these perplexing patterns. We could list Hunter's challenges as poor concentration, hostility, bullying, quarrelsomeness, low frustration, temper outbursts, disobedience, distractibility, impulsivity, spaciness, vacillation between lack of motivation and over stimulation, processing and expressing language — and the list goes on. But we could also list his strengths, including his insatiable interest in math, any subject on the Discovery Channel, and other things that reflected and used his intelligence. Early memories of a teenage reading of Kahlil Gibran's *The Prophet* now took on new meaning.

"[Children] are the sons and daughters of Life's longing for itself."

"They come *through* [us] but *not from* [us]." [1923 by Alfred A. Knopf.]

Their lives are uniquely their own. They are not clones of us. Yet, I yearned to find the key to unlock the mystery of Hunter's behavior. Were Larry and I to blame? Were we failing him as parents in ways that we didn't realize?

I began looking for written information — always my initial instinct — but could find nothing in book stores or libraries. During this pre-Internet era, I finally discovered a graduate-school paper written by the mother of one of Hunter's classmates about the challenges of parenting children with Attention Deficit Disorder (ADD) and Attention Deficit Hyperactive Disorder (ADHD). A couple of years later, in 1984, Dr. Larry Silver, a child and adolescent psychiatrist, published *The Misunderstood Child*, a book that addressed learning disabilities and ADD. But for me, Silver's most profound message was, "*You must do everything in your power to become…an assertive advocate for your child.*" (Silver, p. ix) I wore his message like a badge. Despite feeling overwhelmed, somehow I was able to garner just enough strength and persistence to push on. I had *to do* something.

Melinda Peril, the psychologist, had suggested we start him on a multi-modal regimen: body movement classes to improve balance and coordination, tutoring in sequencing to improve reading, help in composing sentences on the computer, individual therapy, get-along groups, organizational skills, language testing, and occupational therapy and tutoring. Hunter never once questioned why we were putting him through such rigors. He always participated willingly and seemed to enjoy these one-on-one sessions, seeing therapists and tutors as people who cared about him and were interested in him. My life began to revolve around getting Hunter to his myriad appointments.

The Friday afternoon sessions with his therapist who helped him with organizational skills involved driving 20 miles in rush-hour traffic only adding to my frustration. Once a week, seven-year old Hunter, two-year old Ashby, and I headed west on Atlanta's perimeter highway. We then veered north for an additional fifteen miles. We often faced rain or an accident and sat idle in rush hour traffic for inordinate amounts of time. Ashby squirmed in his car seat and whined after strewing Cheerios around the back seat like confetti and we were late almost every week. I always slumped into a chair in the waiting room to gather my wits for the ride home while I made sure Ashby didn't break knickknacks on the coffee table. Meanwhile, Hunter was learning to sort puzzle pieces by color and to type sentences on a computer.

Despite all these efforts, we continued to receive disturbing reports about Hunter's school work. When Hunter entered first grade, we transferred him to a small school that accepted children with ADD or dyslexia and focused on learning to read. We were impressed with the individualized approach. Teachers would analyze each child's learning style and ensure that s/he could connect to reading. Hunter's teacher knew how to work with children with short attention spans, allowing them to go outside and climb on the old dead oak tree as an incentive to help restless students complete their assignments. It was not long before Hunter was getting the main idea of reading. Yet even there, he continued to fall behind.

One of Hunter's teachers wrote on a report card in second grade:

> Audio processing is still a weak area and we must continue to monitor Hunter closely to make sure he is tuned-in. We also see weakness in his spelling and are encouraging him to pay closer

attention to what he is writing in order to cut down on careless spelling and punctuation errors.

The headmaster penned her own harried comments in red: "*Composition and sentence answers are weak. If not improved he will soon receive LOW MARKS.*"

The headmaster disapproved of stimulant medication, like Ritalin, for any child. But the behavior modifications and physical exercise recommended by his teachers were not solving the problem. And so, after mild threats and repeated references to Hunter's inattention by the teacher and headmaster, we consulted our pediatrician — a new, carefully selected one this time — and he prescribed Ritalin. Unbeknownst to the school, we started Hunter on the drug. The next and final report card for the year read as follows:

> Hunter has had a fabulous year and has made great strides of progress. The greatest improvement we've seen has been his audio-processing and his attentiveness in class. He has become a very conscientious student.

Clearly Ritalin had helped Hunter attend better, despite the Headmaster's views. Once again, we had to find our own path through the maze of confusing disagreements among practitioners.

Although Hunter was doing better in school, he still lacked motivation; he was lethargic, and struggled with social relationships. He was never malicious, but he was socially clueless. He never seemed to connect with his peers.

We planned fun birthday parties like rafting and picnicking on the Chattahoochee River, attending a Braves baseball game, creating Slip-and-Slide parties, and organizing a spider-web party with rolls of string strung out through the woods for the children to re-wind to get to a pack of gum—all huge successes judging from the children's reactions. During these parties, Hunter participated but was never in the middle of the activities. He tended to be on the sidelines. The other kids enjoyed the parties but did not become Hunter's friends. However, he was rarely bullied. Sometimes he was invited to other children's birthday parties, perhaps at their parents' insistence, but he was most always delighted to attend.

Still, there were times when he had more direct conflicts with peers. In the second grade, Hunter endured months of bullying from John who was in his carpool—never once standing up for himself. One day, Hunter had had enough and lunged over the seatback and bloodied the boy's nose. Embarrassed and horrified, I scurried into John's house for a damp cloth. Three years later, when they were both attending another school, John continued his bullying. Again, Hunter tolerated it for a while but then one day, he again hurdled over a seat on the bus and slugged John. Although they did not condone fighting, his teachers quietly applauded Hunter for finally overcoming his passivity and defending himself.

Not surprisingly, this was a stressful time for me. I was still caring for Ashby who was an infant toddler while trying to manage Hunter, a challenging child to supervise. I was always tired and took frequent naps. For as long as I can remember, I had always needed a lot of sleep.

Several times through the years my mother had told me, "Your father asks me periodically if sleep is the most important thing in my life. I admitted that *yes*, it is." I could identify with her. And for me, the longing for sleep was even stronger as I struggled to care for two challenging children.

Breast feeding Ashby, I could plan to do only one activity each half a day. I knew women who had returned to work and came home at lunchtime to nurse their babies. I had definitely made the right choice not to juggle a career and motherhood. But being a stay-at-home mom in and of itself was far more challenging than I had imagined. And ironically, it seemed as if I *did* have a full-time career — caring for Hunter and Ashby.

Larry and I seldom went to movies any more. I was concerned that teenagers would not be able to handle Hunter's erratic behavior like jumping from chair to chair around the living room. Besides, arranging for babysitters took initiative and energy which I had a hard time mustering. It was often simpler to just stay home.

Meanwhile, we continued to try to find the best educational setting for Hunter. In fourth grade, Hunter transferred to another private elementary school. The school offered a transition program for children with learning disabilities but was also a college preparatory school. Even though Hunter found school challenging, his IQ scores were always in the superior range, a perplexing combination rolled into one person. These inconsistencies were evident in the following answer that he wrote on a test in sixth grade:

> The differences the man had were that it was in a desert. They had
> to dig wells with their bare hands. It was a drout (sic) and most

of the wells were dry. He thought that he didn't think of paying because water is offered freely in America. He drank four bowls ment (sic) two (sic) wash his feet.

This was an improvement over his first few essay tests in which he eked out only one sentence. But what did he mean? One frustrated teacher scratched on a test, "*I refuse to grade this. It is illegible. I know you can write better.*"

Still another teacher said to me at a parent conference, that at the end of each day she always hoped she had said more positive things to Hunter than negative. I knew my mother never experienced such school conferences with *my* teachers. Why did he face such challenges?

With time, it became increasingly apparent that Hunter's peers were beginning to soar, and he was inching along on a bumpy road with numerous falls, like his trip through the snowy woods. Now, as I re-read the list of tests and therapies, including the multi-modal approach recommended by the psychologist, I am aghast at the number of interventions we tried. Although many professionals were helpful, our quest also took us down some futile paths.

In 1989 when Hunter was twelve, a friend who happened to be an adult psychiatrist, asked me at a dinner party if we had ever taken Hunter to a child psychiatrist. I assumed he thought we were wasting our time with psychologists and tutors and other non-MD types. We soon scheduled an appointment with someone he recommended. Once again, I harbored the same feelings as I did before our first meeting with a pediatric neurologist: taking our twelve-year old son to a *psychiatrist?*

At our first appointment with her, Larry and I described our seven-year odyssey trying to find out what was wrong. Hunter met with her alone the following week, and Larry and I went to the third meeting to hear her observations and recommendations. I jotted notes on a yellow legal pad during her monologue:

> Slow speech—inarticulate with his level of intelligence—frequently distracted, internally—not good at abstract questions—thinks concretely—not unhappy with so few friends—does not understand good humor—primary problem: more social (not L.D. or A.D.D.) almost psychotic—out of touch with reality—quasi-internally—in his own world—signs are clear. *HE'S A CHILDHOOD SCHIZOPHRENIC.*
>
> Social isolation is going to continue—don't push sociability—respect his needs.

"*Childhood schizophrenic?*" I blurted numbly. "Where can I read about *that?*"

She could not give me or recommend any references. After a pacing, hand-wringing weekend and much conversation with Larry, I called her office Monday morning. "Is there *any* material at the Emory Medical School library—or *any*where?" (At the time there was still no Internet.)

After a long silence, the psychiatrist replied, "Try Oxford Book Store or Borders Book Store. If you find something good, *let me know.*" And she hung up.

Let her know? I quickly tallied how many hundreds of dollars we had paid for this cavalier response. Come on, *let her know?*

After three hours, I left the book stores with the only references to childhood schizophrenia I could find: the *Merck Manual* and the *DSM III*. From the descriptions, neither Larry nor I believed this diagnosis, nor did the educational consultants and therapists who had been working with Hunter. Once again, a doctor had stoked my mounting mistrust of the medical profession.

Meanwhile, Ashby was starting school, and we hoped that he would have an easier time of it than Hunter. Shortly after his second birthday, Ashby started attending pre-school twice a week, in the same school Hunter had attended for two years of kindergarten. We thought Ashby quite accomplished because he was one of only two children potty-trained on the first day of school! Although it was not the right school for Hunter, Larry and I rejoiced that this small, private school seemed an excellent fit for Ashby. He was a gregarious, self-confident little fellow who was often invited home to play with friends and spend the night. When he was 5-6 years old, he frequently went on a friend's family vacations to the beach. Mothers always reported glowingly about Ashby as a houseguest. He was a happy child with an uncanny awareness of the world around him. One day when he was two and a half, I told him we were going to the grocery store. "Okay," he piped up cheerily, "I'll get your list, your purse, and your keys." To our joy, Ashby seemed to be off to a successful start.

Sadly, this propitious beginning did not last. In pre-K, Ashby had trouble learning to read. At first, we dismissed these concerns; Larry assured me that Ashby would have a secretary when he grew up. However, in second grade, he was still not reading well, even though he had attended pre-K twice. He was now sent down the hall to the reading tutor every day and *hated* be-ing separated from his peers. His struggles and frustrations were clear to us the first day he was given homework. He eagerly sat at his desk. He was now a *big boy*! However, after five minutes he slammed his pencil down. "*I thought this was going to be fun — but it's not!*"

He soon started telling us routinely that he *hated* school. He would ask his teacher for permission to go to the bathroom and not return. She'd later find him swinging on the bathroom door. Alas, it turned out this school was not a good fit for Ashby either. At first grade, we switched him to a school for children with language difficulties. Ironically, in his class of nine, three had fathers who were architects. He was very unhappy there, so the next year we switched him to another school for children with special needs. He went there for grades 2-5 and had excellent teachers during that time. In 6th grade, he moved to a private prep school which seemed to be a good fit for him.

As we struggled to find schools and programs that would work for our children, we kept wondering, "What *was* the problem?" As a child, I had flowed in and out of numerous schools. No big deal. Larry, despite the tragic loss of his mother, had had no significant problems in school. Why couldn't Hunter and Ashby simply go with the flow? Did we hover too close? My own mother gave us space to figure out things on our own, and we usually did. But neither Hunter nor Ashby seemed equipped to do so.

Even though I was often exhausted by these challenges and discouraged by many blind alleys, a persistent, nagging voice inside propelled me on my quest to know, like a scientist who *must* know what's inside the nucleus of a cell or what lies beyond our galaxy. Why do people climb mountains? Because they are *there*! And Hunter was *there*, our long-awaited first-born child in all his wonderful and enigmatic ways. And Ashby was *there*, caught between his social success and his academic struggles.

5. Answers Begin to Emerge

Despite my exhaustion and the complexities of meeting the needs of both boys, I knew that I had to develop my own life and passion to survive. As I had done for the past decade, I continued volunteering with the Junior League. But I found little satisfaction in logging in requisite hours for a project conjured up and organized by someone else. Besides, I was now over forty, and my years with the Junior League were coming to a close.

In 1983, Larry had started his own architectural firm. It was inevitable with his self-confidence as a leader, with his energy and drive as a big-picture thinker. "I need to be captain of my own ship, even if it's a dinghy," he uttered. And so, with a colleague from the airport project, they founded Lord & Sargent. Even though they decided to forego a salary for six months, I didn't fret. I had confidence that Larry would grow the firm quickly and would soon have enough people to field a softball team! He never regretted his decision and never looked back. Neither did I.

I, too, needed to be captain of my own ship and was hungry for something more in my life. I had majored in and taught English, kept journals, and dabbled in poetry. My favorite writing form is letters; I would pore over letters that I composed and, on occasion, edit those that Larry wrote. Writing took me deep inside myself: grappling with new perceptions, feelings, questions, and conflicts, shifting me to a different place and time, sometimes causing me to forget lunch, as I immersed myself in and reaped the benefits from the *process*. I registered for a short-story writing course at Georgia State University's downtown campus. It attracted many students like me: older and *there* because we *wanted* to be. Not only did the course provide the space and encouragement for me to write, it also helped me to develop a broader and more honest perspective on my life as a mother.

One of my short stories, titled *Gravity*, told of a career woman who, after years of trying to conceive, finally succeeds. The frustration of a colicky baby and a workaholic husband culminates one night when she hurls a shampoo bottle out of the shower and shatters her favorite Limoges dish. The story concludes:

> Breathing faster, you continue standing under the pulsating stream. The hot water finally turns warm, then tepid. At last you turn it off. The baby in her husband's arms outside the bathroom has finally stopped screaming. Stepping out of the shower, you try to avoid the shards, but a tiny sliver lodges in your foot. It smarts; it bleeds, but you ignore it as you habitually do in so many situations; you grab a towel and open the door; the cold air embraces your flesh. It feels clean and clear and sounds silent. And then the pull begins drawing at you like one of the irrefutable laws of nature.

One day on our walk back to the parking deck from our writing class, Mitzi, a friend and classmate, and I were discussing the autobiographical aspects of the short stories we had read aloud that day. Her story's young, up-beat protagonist reminded me of her son who was Hunter's age. "Well, maybe," she hedged. "I suppose I just have an *exalted* feeling about my children."

I will never forget that word, *exalted*.

I stopped, faced her, stood silent, and finally spoke. "Hunter is — an *enigma* — and feels like — like — an *albatross* around my neck."

She stood speechless. We turned and walked in silence the rest of the way to our cars.

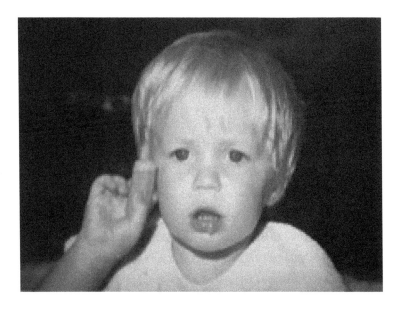

One day, as I passed the gallery of family photos in our house, a picture of Hunter at age two caught my eye. He was holding a Vienna sausage close to his cheek; his golden locks falling toward his face are long and tousled, his expression contemplative, and his mouth open with a drool hanging from his lower lip. It was the drool that always made me smile. Several years after it was taken, I had asked the pediatrician why his mouth was always open. He suggested allergies and wrote a prescription for nose drops. The drops did nothing to change Hunter. Another misdiagnosis…

In 1989, when Hunter was 12, Larry and I attended a talk at his school given by Dr. Nick Krawiecki, a pediatric neurologist and expert in attentional problems. He showed PET scans of brains of children with attentional disabilities and pointed out that these problems stem from lack of stimulation. After we heard him speak, we looked at each other and I said, "We really need to go and talk with him." Three months later, as I prepared for the appointment, I sent Dr. Krawiecki an introduction to Hunter and described our seven-year odyssey to find an explanation for our concerns. I concluded,

> We have discovered after dealing with the whole L.D.-A.D.D.
> spectrum (which has been aptly described as "not a science but an
> art") that the different categories of professionals who deal with
> problems of the brain are like political camps. It becomes difficult
> for parents to know which one to join: medication vs. no medica-
> tion; small, structured schools vs. mainstreaming.

Larry adjusted his schedule so he could attend the appointment. Dr. Krawiecki examined Hunter then held up two fingers, instructing Hunter to squeeze them. Hunter cooperated but was unable to release his grip. After a few more questions for Hunter, a thump on his tongue and the fatty part of his thumb, the doctor said, "See? This is *myotonia*. When he contracts his voluntary muscles, they do not relax on command." He returned to his desk, asked a few questions and jotted down answers with his Mont Blanc pen. Then he asked Hunter if he liked TV. Hunter reacted with excitement as Dr. Krawiecki took him to a special area where he could watch TV, a much preferred activity than being with yet another doctor. After a few minutes, Dr. Krawiecki returned, sat again at his desk, breathed deeply, and leaned forward in his chair. "Mr. and Mrs. Lord, is there any history of *muscle disease* in your family?"

"Muscle disease—hmm—*muscle disease*?" I pondered.

After some thought, Larry responded, "No, not in mine."

During what seemed like forever, my mind darted frenetically from names to faces in the different branches of my family. Suddenly an image of my Cousin Helen emerged. I had a flashback to the first autumn after my family had moved back to Mobile. One of my great aunts called my mother to offer me her granddaughter's barely worn, red evening dress that was stored at her house. During our visit, I met her daughter Helen for the first time. She was in her fifties, lying in bed with her longtime companion Mary sitting nearby. When we were introduced, Helen extended a thin arm and grabbed my hand. She uttered something indiscernible. Her grasp was tight, and it seemed that she didn't want to let go.

"I beg your pardon?" I said as I tried to remove my hand. She was sort of scary. I wanted to bolt. Instead, I screwed my courage and leaned in closer, trying to decipher her garbled speech. I glared at my mother with an adolescent, "why-did-you-bring-me-here?" look. I finally figured a polite way to disengage.

As I thought about Helen, I recalled one of the late-night chats I often had with my mother. Out of the blue, she said, "Your father's family has physical ailments like a crushed disc or appendicitis—you know—operable things. But my Hunter family has all sorts of inoperable things." In addition to Helen, my mother told stories of other eccentric Hunter relatives. Although my great uncle was a talented musician and boat builder, he was a recluse. Even though he lived only a few blocks from us, I never met him. He got married as a young man but continued living at home until one day his mother discovered his wedding ring in his sock drawer.

Then there was Athalee, my second cousin who attended my high school. She had a strange gait, thick glasses, poor dental hygiene, and lipstick out-of-the-lines. She often made pronouncements like, "Last night, John Wayne asked me for a date." I was not proud of my feelings, but I viewed her as out-of-touch with reality; I simply couldn't relate to her and I admitted our kinship to very few. I vividly remember her mother with a long, expressionless face, droopy eyelids, and open mouth as she clung to the steering wheel of her baby blue Comet puttering around town. She had to Scotch tape her eyelids open so she could see to drive. My mother commented nostalgically one night, "Athalee used to be so beautiful." Another cousin once asked for permission to bring Athalee to a family wedding because she didn't get invited many places. Mama then shook her head and stared away. "Where in all of this is human decency?" The sadness in her voice still resonates in me.

Another great aunt had a special table where she kept odd bits of string and thread she found lying around or clinging to her clothes. One Christmas she sent a small gift, wrapped in a wrinkled, brown grocery bag addressed to both of my parents. To everyone's amazement—especially my father's—out rolled two used lipsticks! The whole family then was known as frugal. Was this an example of their thrift, or did this unusual gift carry some other meaning?

Of course, there were numerous other Hunter relatives devoid of notable quirks who had been successful in many ways. They made me feel better; I stood with them. Even those with eccentricities bore little resemblance to one another, except they "weren't quite right." My mother intimated several times that they probably all had the Hunter disease, an odd assortment of symptoms that afflicted several relatives who tended to lead somewhat isolated, sedentary, sometimes rather sickly lives.

The toll that this disease took was epitomized by Cousin Helen. Like my mother, Helen loved the water. She had been an excellent diver and had spent summers at Camp Greystone in North Carolina, later working there as a camp counselor. One particular night as we sat talking, my mother paused, her demeanor changed, she spoke in a stage whisper: "Helen probably has the worst form of the Hunter disease." Then she added, almost like a prayer of petition, "I truly hope you five children will be spared."

"Mom!" I interrupted. "Think about it! We're all strong and athletic! Surely we don't have what she has!" I knew with every award, every easy victory in the classroom, and every wonderful night on the dance floor, I was not like Helen. The subject was not mentioned again for years.

"Is there any history of muscle disease in your family?" Dr. Krawiecki patiently asked again.

Again, Larry said, "No."

"Maybe…" I said, barely able to eke out a sound.

He looked us directly in the eye. "It appears that Hunter has *myotonic dystrophy*—a type of muscular dystrophy. But we must confirm this diagnosis with an EMG. All of you need to have the test. You need to call Dr. Hopkins' office and schedule…"

The doctor's words—*my-o-to-nic-dys-tro-phy*—were nothing more than staccato syllables, meaningless, empty, nothing, nada. I had never heard these words. Considering myself to be quite observant, I was shocked that I had never noticed the stiffness in Hunter's hands. Was this why he refused to look a stranger in the eye and offer a firm handshake, in spite of repeated coaxing to teach him good manners as Larry and I had been taught? But *this* symptom was *not* the one that prompted us to consult a neurologist. What about all of Hunter's other problems?

As Larry and I walked back to the car with Hunter lollygagging behind as usual, Larry puzzled through a grimace, *"Muscular dystrophy?"*

"No. He said *myotonic* dystrophy. He won't be in a wheel chair—at least I don't think he will."

But what did I know?

We continued walking in silence, each carrying our own fear of a diagnosis about which we knew nothing. This doctor had identified an observable symptom—and named it. No doubt he was on to something. But, really, what did Hunter's handshake have to do with his learning profile and puzzling behavior? And why would we all need to be tested?

Marking time until the next appointment never grew easier, and waiting for the EMG (electromyography) with Dr. Hopkins was no exception. Weeks later, Hunter lay supine on the neurologist's table next to a monitor. The neurology fellow inserted a needle into his leg muscle and jiggled it. When the muscle contracted, he looked for a certain pattern on the screen and a dive-bomber sound. Each time the needle was inserted Hunter winced and squeezed two fingers tightly against my ring finger. It hurt. The monitor quickly registered the results the doctor was looking for and confirmed Dr. Krawiecki's tentative diagnosis of *myotonic dystrophy*.

Then it was my turn. As I lay on the table, the fellow inserted and jiggled the needle in a lower leg muscle and then another, and another, up one side and down the other. Like Hunter, I winced at every jiggle. But there was no dive-bomber sound. Not finding the results he was looking for, the neurology fellow furrowed his brow and scratched his head. Short of a muscle biopsy, this was the only diagnostic test at the time. He discussed the results with another neurology fellow; both shrugged. Next, they tested Larry; and, as we expected, he exhibited no myotonia.

In the week that followed, I learned enough about the disease and my family to know that if Hunter had myotonic dystrophy, Larry or I had to have it also. If a child has myotonic dystrophy, almost without exception, one parent carries this dominant gene. If a child does not inherit one parent's mutant gene, then his children and subsequent generations need not worry. It does not go underground like a recessive gene only to resurface generations later. Even with negative test results, I never doubted I had the disease.

At our appointment, Dr. Hopkins informed us that scientists were trying to isolate the myotonic dystrophy gene. When it was located, he felt certain a new test would be developed and reveal a positive diagnosis in me. I asked for more information about our disease. In a heartbeat, he returned with a book from a professional series on neurological disorders. Recalling earlier fruitless searches, I smiled appreciatively as I copied the publisher's name and address. During this pre-Internet period, there was no Amazon.com or two-day delivery. Finally, ninety dollars and months later, *Myotonic Dystrophy*, 1st Edition, the definitive book on the disease by Dr. Peter Harper, an internationally acclaimed geneticist at the University of Cardiff in Wales, arrived.

I was grateful for the book, known informally as *the big book*, but admittedly found that much of the information was far too complex for one without medical training. I had skirted through school with as few science courses as possible, and, although I read and re-read most of the volume, much eluded me. Nonetheless, I highlighted passages, looked up definitions, wrote notes in margins and marked important pages with post-its. Continuing to wear the mantle as my child's mother and advocate, I assumed the challenge of educating myself, then Hunter's teachers and doctors, most of whom had never heard of myotonic dystrophy. Dr. Harper's book accompanied me everywhere.

I learned that myotonic dystrophy (often referred to as DM1 or DM, the acronym for the Latin name, *dystrophia myotonica*) is a rare, inherited, chronic, slowly degenerative, multi-systemic disease that can present at any age. It is one of nine diseases under the umbrella of the muscular dystrophies and is often described as *the most common form of adult-onset muscular dystrophy*. It affects approximately 1 in 8,000 people world-wide. From person to person—even within the same family—age of onset and types and severity of symptoms can differ. Some people may be so mildly affected that they may never know they have the disease until a relative with more severe symptoms is diagnosed. Others may suffer from not only skeletal muscle weakness, stiffness, and atrophy, but also smooth muscle weakness as along the GI tract. It can cause heart arrhythmias, sometimes resulting in sudden death, as well as serious brain, gastrointestinal, and endocrine impairment. DM is often described by age of onset: congenital, juvenile, or adult-onset. If one inherits this dominant gene, she or he has the disease, although in some people it presents with only mild symptoms like early cataracts. Many people with the disease lead long, normal lives. Some may be completely mobile, but others may eventually need motorized scooters. So, I realized I was wrong about no wheelchairs in my reassurance to Larry as we left Dr. Krawiecki's office.

Women and men with the gene may be unaware they even have the disease, but they frequently give birth to children who have it. Hypotonic (floppy) infants have the most severe congenital form. Often these children are unable to breathe and feed and may die at birth. Many people with this gene have less severe symptoms and live to grow up but struggle with excessive daytime sleepiness, lack of motivation and initiative, though these symptoms do not necessarily correlate with the severity of muscle weakness. Because of central nervous system involvement, some affected individuals find it difficult to assume responsibility for many aspects of their lives—making doctors' appointments and showing up, keeping up with prescriptions, eating nutritional meals, paying bills—and are unable to live independently. Dr. Krawiecki's tentative diagnosis, corroborated by the findings of Dr. Hopkins' neurology fellows, along with the information I was reading, painted a disturbing picture. But, fortunately for us, Dr. Krawiecki and Dr. Hopkins were kind and compassionate throughout the diagnostic process. They were *present* every step of the way; they looked us in the eye; they *listened* well; they were compassionate and knowledgeable about the disease. And Dr. Krawiecki's sense of humor and levity during Hunter's subsequent appointments helped carry us through the next few years. Our dealings with these two doctors were radically different from our initial foray into the world of neurology.

Finally, after eight years of searching, we had a correct diagnosis for Hunter. Where would we go from here?

6. Genetics: The Root Cause

We now understood the source of Hunter's problems, but many questions remained—questions that Ashby forced us to face.

Two or three years after Hunter's diagnosis, Ashby was at his second school for children with special needs and having difficulty getting along with his fifth-grade teacher, as well as several classmates. After a few months, we sought professional help, and after a number of weekly sessions, the child psychologist shared Ashby's primary concern: It had nothing to do with his teacher or classmates. It had everything to do with his *fear that someday he would be just like his brother.* At the end of the appointment, she asked if there was a way to find out if Ashby also had myotonic dystrophy. I nodded affirmatively and told her that I thought a test had been developed. She urged us to have him tested.

Since early childhood, Ashby had a keen awareness of himself and the world around him. He no doubt observed Hunter at close range: his open mouth; his face slowly assuming a blunt affect. He knew that his brother had few friends and attended a special school because of learning difficulties. Hunter had also been ruthless to Ashby from his first day home from the hospital and continued to tease Ashby while they were both young. Ashby was increasingly embarrassed by Hunter and dreaded the possibility that he might become like him.

Even after Hunter's diagnosis, I did not believe Ashby had it. To be honest, I did not *want* to face that possibility. But Ashby had his own learning issues; he lacked focus, impulse control, and motivation. One of my siblings had had difficulties in school as well and did not graduate from college. Like Hunter and me, in fact like my mother and all my siblings, Ashby struggled to get up in the morning. All these symptoms, I had learned, *could* be caused by DM. However, unlike Hunter, Ashby's motor development was age appropriate, in fact, quite good. Also, unlike Hunter, Ashby was keenly aware of others and almost socially gifted. He understood body language, facial expressions, and other non-verbal cues. Early on he seemed wise beyond his years. During our search for an elementary school for him, he was interviewed by the director of one program who said she looked forward to meeting *this little paragon*—an impression she inferred from several of her students who had previously gone to school with him.

Even though Ashby appeared to be free of the more obvious DM symptoms, the question of whether Ashby was affected was on the table. The boys' pediatrician knew of Hunter's diagnosis and, to my delight, had added the hand grip test to all his patients' annual physicals. He, too, had puzzled aloud a time or two, "You don't think Ashby has it, too, do you?"

Twenty years after Ashby was in the fifth grade, he told me that one day during that year he was blithely tossing a closed container of Jell-O pudding in the air as he walked down the stairs. Suddenly he missed, and pudding splattered everywhere. That incident made him think he was losing strength and coordination in his hands and was becoming like Hunter. After all, Ashby had always been the agile, athletic one, like my hall-of-fame father. The incident on the stairs could have happened to anyone, but to Ashby it was a terrifying sign.

By 1992, researchers had identified the gene and the mutation that caused DM, so we now knew we could do genetic testing to determine which one of us had DM. We were eager to learn about Ashby and still curious about my negative EMG results, so without much ado, Larry and I decided to test the entire family. No one in the medical community tried to *dis*courage us, nor did anyone *en*courage us to consult a geneticist. The world of genetics was so new; I didn't even know what a geneticist was at the time. Once again, it did not occur to us to ask a doctor for advice. I blithely ordered testing kits from the University of Alabama Medical School in Birmingham (UAB) and we had our blood drawn at the hospital at Emory University. Hunter and Ashby went along with the tests, seeming to feel they were nothing special.

Coincidentally, the scientist at UAB who was conducting the DNA tests informed me that Dr. Peter Harper would be speaking about recent research and treatment options for DM at the UAB medical school in a few weeks. I drove two and a half hours to UAB to hear the author of *the big book* that had become my faithful companion. I comprehended little of Dr. Harper's "medicalese" that closely echoed his book, but at the conclusion of his speech, I shyly approached the stage. He was the author of the definitive writings, not only on myotonic dystrophy, but also on Huntington's disease. I was awed to be in the presence of a man of such stature in the medical world. He stood there with his hands in his pockets and occasionally glanced at the floor. He struck me as a highly intelligent, dedicated, but very humble physician, author, and researcher. I was delighted to meet him for the first of the many times that would follow, although I had no idea at the time.

From Dr. Harper I learned that the disease was caused by the number of CTG repeats. These letters stand for *cytosine, thymine and guanine,* three chemicals (out of possibly four, the fourth being *adenine)* repeated in a sequence side-by side in the DNA (deoxyribonucleic acid). This string of chemicals, also called the expansion, is laid out in this order in the DMPK gene and is located on chromosome 19. The number of expanded repeats running along the rung-like parts of the DNA ladder indicates the size of the genetic defect. Everyone has this gene, and up to thirty-seven sets of CTG repeats are normal. Thirty-eight to 50 repeats indicate an unstable number; one may or may not have myotonic dystrophy, and offspring may or may not inherit the disease. But with more than fifty, the person has an inherited mutation or abnormality in the gene that causes myotonic dystrophy.

Filled with anxiety about what the results of the testing would show and, in particular, whether or not Ashby had DM, I then went to the lab at UAB to get them. As I took the report, I forced my eyes to focus on the lines that revealed our number of CTG repeats. As we expected, Larry's repeats fell within the normal range. Hunter's repeats numbered 350. Mine were 167. This news was no real surprise to me. I knew I had to have it. And then I read Ashby's. His... 183.

After reviewing them with the UAB scientist who had run the tests, I stuffed them into my purse—completely devastated.

Now I had to drive back to Atlanta alone, carrying this weight. And back then I had no cell phone, so I could not call Larry. Exceeding the speed limit, I raced up the highway, all the while wondering how my sons would react to the news. I reflected on Hunter's calm acceptance of his diagnosis after the EMG. The very characteristics of aloofness and lack of awareness—like an absent-minded professor—that got him in trouble with teachers, peers, and his brother, is also what often saved him.

But Ashby was different; he was an observant, thinking, feeling child. How would he react to this diagnosis?

Larry and I had decided beforehand to tell him the results, but we stalled for a couple of weeks, not knowing quite how to tell Ashby that he had the disease. I now watched him even more closely on the soccer field: every punt, every save, every header. I studied him before awakening him every morning: his corn-silk locks, his fair skin, his pale pink birthmark on one eyelid, his peaceful state as he slept. And I observed him interacting appropriately with children in the carpool.

Without a diagnosis, he was decidedly anxious about *not* knowing, and, whether or not he had it, he was equally anxious about his inadequacy in the classroom and feeling *different* from his peers. However, I was truly concerned about how he would react when he learned that he did in fact have DM. As usual, Ashby forced the issue. After school one late winter afternoon, with the western sun splayed across our dining room table, Ashby piped up, "Oh, Mom—by the way—what about those tests?"

"What tests?" I stopped short as I grabbed the back of a chair.

"You know—those *blood* tests."

"Oh," I hesitated, "those!" pausing to take a deep breath and mustering everything I had to appear nonchalant. "As a matter of fact, we just got the results back."

"Well," he wasted no time, "do I have it?"

I cleared my throat, hesitated a moment and chose my words carefully. "Yes, you have it—but sort of like I do. Your gene is a tiny bit bigger than mine, but not much; Hunter's is almost twice as big—that's why he has it worse."

A smile came over him, as he looked at my hands that he knew painted, sewed, gardened, and did all sorts of other things. "You mean—it's like—I really *don't* have it?"

"Exactly!" I smiled. "And I lead a pretty normal life, don't you think?"

End of conversation. He resumed playing with the dog, watching TV, and exhibiting no signs of concern.

I recalled advice from older parents when my children were young: "Never tell a child more than he wants to know." One day several months before Ashby was born, Hunter, then four and half, asked me just how that baby got into my tummy. I thought long and hard before I replied. After my first cautious explanation, Hunter asked how the fertilizer got in there. "Did you *swallow* it?" No sooner had I answered, again with carefully chosen words, than he resumed looking for a Lego for his spaceship. Based on this experience, I assumed Ashby had heard enough, was satisfied, and went about his afternoon. Very little was ever mentioned again about myotonic dystrophy. It took us years to realize how masterfully Ashby concealed his anxieties and how his desire to *just be normal* like his peers drove him to become increasingly recalcitrant toward us, his teachers, his peers, and to seek out risky activities.

So, we now knew the root cause, we now knew what was wrong. Thus, ended our odyssey of discovery. Our inquisitiveness, dedication, and perseverance had led us to our initial goal. Yet, sadly, we had also learned that we could not fix it. We could only learn to live with the reality that our family, especially our sons, would be forever defined by one defective gene.

PART II

LIVING WITH A DEFECTIVE GENE

7. My Story

*Initially, I was able to stave off the emotional impact of inher-*iting a multisystemic disease and passing it on to my children. Before our diagnosis, I had busied myself in intellectual pursuits to try to identify the problem. Now I was energized to learn more about the disease and how to mitigate its effects. I read many books and learned as much as I could. But it was simply a matter of time before my feelings would force their way to the surface as the enormity of the revelation slowly seeped into my conscious-ness and daily life.

When I first learned about the disease, I had silently vowed, "This disease will *not* change my life. It will *not…*" However, I found myself beginning to wobble and stumble, fending off an invisible, unadulterated *fear of the diagnosis* itself, as if it were going to erupt and consume me. Well-meaning friends tried to compare my situation to others that were much worse and to talk me out of my feelings. A Hunter cousin glibly offered, "Well, we're all going to die of something." I had begun to feel that something was already dying inside of me, and I was unable to digest and take comfort from this well-intended offering. I was burdened by the awareness that I had passed this defective gene on to my sons; I was filled with sadness. There were no magic bullets. The boys would have to live with this disease for the rest of their lives. Despite all my efforts to identify and learn about this disease, I realized that nothing we could do would change the futures of Ashby and Hunter's life with myotonic dystrophy.

Soon I realized there was nowhere to go or be, except into my sadness. I did not want to linger *in* it forever; yet I also knew that I could not skirt *around* it, *over* or *under* it; I knew I had to go *through* it. Our concerns now had a *name*, and I could begin the grieving process. No one could have convinced me nor could I have ever imagined the empowerment that would eventually emerge merely from *naming* the disorder. Now, at age forty-three, I was forced to look squarely into the face of life's finiteness, my own mortality, something we all must do but often not until we're much older.

The magnitude of our diagnosis had now begun casting a dark shadow over all my life. Each day I got out of bed, put one foot in front of the other, and shuffled my way through the morning: breakfast, Hunter and Larry off at 7:10 A.M., Ashby up, breakfast, sack lunch, carpool, errands, dishes, and laundry. Afterwards, I dimmed the lights and slumped into the living room sofa where I would remain until I had to pick up Ashby from school. I gave up all household responsibilities. Mail and newspapers began piling up; bills came past due. We hired a maid to keep the house clean and organized. I could not write anything. Not even a sentence. I gave up the one commitment I had claimed for myself, my writing course at Georgia State. I felt alone because

Larry, with his can-do attitude, never got down. Every morning he bounced out of bed, got Hunter up and dressed, fed, and on the school bus and then went to work, whereas I could barely get up from the sofa.

Despite my depression and lethargy, I was determined that Hunter would have whatever tutors and support he needed, but my efforts often seemed futile. Hunter continued working with the educational consultant twice a week on organizational skills. She was very helpful, but his teachers did not understand the cause of Hunter's problems nor our efforts to support him. One educator had insinuated that, by focusing on his disease, we were teaching Hunter *learned helplessness*. By this time, we were able to take this kind of comment with a grain of salt.

Shortly after Dr. Krawiecki's tentative diagnosis, I had requested a brochure on myotonic dystrophy from the Muscular Dystrophy Association; but the information answered few of my questions. I attended an MDA general support group meeting, but I was the only person there with myotonic dystrophy. Others in the group were primarily dealing with physical issues; no one there was similar to Hunter, who was mobile but out of the mainstream and without friends, and unable to live up to expectations for someone of his age.

I was determined to get as much help as we could for Hunter, but these efforts were taxing on all of us. Often Ashby, who was now 11 years old, and I would meet Hunter's yellow bus at 4:15 PM, crawl through fifteen miles of traffic for a 5 PM appointment with Sherry, his educational consultant, and arrive home at 7 PM, exhausted, with dinner yet to prepare and homework and baths to be negotiated. One rainy January afternoon, after a nerve-wracking drive through slippery streets with Hunter and Ashby fighting in the back seat as usual, we arrived at Sherry's office. Ashby found a game to play while I attempted to distract myself. Having forgotten to bring a book, I picked up a magazine in the waiting room and thumbed through it. Then another. And another. Realizing that I was simply going through motions, I set the magazines down and stared blankly at the wall until Hunter and Sherry reappeared. Numb and robot-like, I made my way toward them.

"Sherry, I can't keep bringing Hunter out here." My words spilled out as tears formed rivulets that trickled down my cheeks and on to my sweater. Putting her arm around me, Sherry nudged me toward her office. My rigid body relaxed into her tender gesture as I sobbed.

She offered a tissue and waited for me to stop, then took a step back, crossed her arms, and said firmly but kindly, "Okay, Shannon. It's time for *you* to *take care of yourself*. Remember the flight attendant's advice: 'Put the oxygen mask on yourself and then on your child.' I have an excellent psychologist to recommend—I mean for *you*. Consider Hunter's work with me complete for now. There is much ahead and you must take care of yourself so you can continue on this frustrating journey."

Take care of myself? But this didn't jive with childhood admonitions of not being self-centered, not focusing too much on myself. As children, we were taught to *love thy neighbor as thyself*. But no one ever focused much on *as thyself*. It soon became clear that I had given and given to my children until I had given out, a state many mothers can relate to, especially those who have children with special needs.

FAMILY ROOTS

I contacted the psychology therapist Sherry recommended, only to find her calendar booked until May. My faith in doctors and other help-professionals had been wavering for several years now, and I would not talk to just *any* psychologist. Sherry had proven herself with Hunter's improvement in organizational skills and I decided her recommendation of this therapist was good advice. I would sit tight until May.

During the ensuing weeks, I felt like an oyster locked in a shell fathoms deep in the sea with no light and no exit. As I lay on the sofa, I could not even bring myself to open my eyes and count the number of boards in the cedar ceiling or the bolts in the trusses. I needed something to focus my mind. I was unable to ignite even a spark of motivation as I lay motionless in this formidable place with no exit. Would I eventually succumb on this teal sofa where I lay inert and helpless? I had learned that people with DM often had issues with motivation, initiation, anxiety, and depression as well as obsessive tendencies. I wondered if my current state was a result of *my* myotonic dystrophy gene.

The days dragged on. Eventually I simply *could — not — tolerate — this — state — any — longer*. One day my *patience* with despair exploded like a punctured balloon, releasing rancid air that reeked of *impatience*. It lurked around me and with every inhalation filled me. I don't remember what happened next or how I came to find myself standing in front of my art cabinet that day. Was it because the unbearable agony had forced the synapses of impatience to finally connect? Or was it remembering some happy solitary, creative childhood event like figuring how to sew a muumuu *all by myself*? Or the memories of the joy I felt when I had carefully arranged shells and sand dollars in descending size on the screened porch of our beach house? I truly can't remember what took me there, but I do recall rummaging through stacks of items that I had used in projects through the years: flowered print from a wrap-around skirt; instructions from the baby-bunting I had knitted for my first niece, silk remnants, metallic threads, buttons, tassels, beads, and an odd assortment of other materials. I began to feel my heart beating with a glimmer of excitement. Maybe, if I started an art project, I would feel more alive, and the pervasive sadness might recede.

At the 19th Century restored farm house where I worked before Hunter was born, I learned not only about flowers but also about textiles of the period. I was fascinated that many farmers and family members who toiled from "kin to cain't," people who lived in absolute survival mode, still harbored an aesthetic sense, an appreciation or perhaps an inner need to incorporate beauty into their lives. In addition to tending their gardens, they spun cotton and wool, dyed and wove them into lovely fabrics on large floor looms. They often adorned their beds with carefully stitched quilts — with wedding ring, honeycomb, and Rose of Sharon patterns — sewn from scraps of worn clothing while in conversation with other women at quilting bees.

I understood this aesthetic pull and had always loved making beautiful things. However, when the boys had come along, my creative impulses and art materials had been stored away for a time when life demanded less of me. Now, as I stood before them for the first time in a long while, I piled a basket full of long-forgotten items, placed a protective cover on the dining room table, and pulled up a chair.

I gazed at what lay before me. Finally, I picked up a silk tassel and dragged it across my arm. It tickled. I held glass beads up to the light and stared into the tiny round sanctums of cobalt, crimson, emerald, colors that another time may have inspired an *ah*. I still had no clue what I would do with this motley collection.

I hung a tassel from my ear and gazed in the mirror.

I placed beads in patterns, in straight lines, in circles, in curved formations.

I looked around some more, searching, imagining.

I looped a piece of upholstery roping around my neck.

I sorted through a pile and threaded a needle. I covered the rope with silk—sewed patterns of gold and silver thread and fastened it with Velcro. I sewed a rosette of fabric, beads, buttons, and tassels and created a flamboyant broach for a basic black dress. I busied myself at the dining room table for the rest of the day. I listened for Hunter and Ashby when they arrived but mostly focused on the disarray before me. Fortunately, at this point the boys did not require much supervision. They would entertain themselves, and maybe they sensed I needed some time for myself.

During the next few weeks I began noticing that I was hastening through my morning routine to get to the dining room table. A slight stir was emerging from my otherwise lifeless body. As I worked on various projects, occasional memories began to emerge: building drip castles on whatever beach I found myself, creating a Halloween diorama with sand and sticks and flowers, and making campaign posters when I ran for high school offices. I sometimes worked till the wee hours on a dress, a skirt, a smocked sun-suit; I lost track of time; I forgot to stop for lunch; I felt good in the doing and proud and satisfied when I completed a project.

Next I made Christmas ornaments that segued into caricatures of middle-aged women with pince-nez glasses on bad-hair days. I placed them in tiny glass boxes with a few loose beads — their lost marbles — for women to wear around their necks. I created them in my own image, and one day the muscles in my face began trying to smile. Myotonic dystrophy is sometimes called *a disease without a smile* due to muscle weakness in the face. I looked in the mirror to make sure I could still smile.

Soon, painted furniture took precedence over women with lost marbles. I began with a small square table and painted a checkerboard on top that was decorated with bird eggs or feathers or constellations. I offered a dollar for each feather my children brought to me. My nephew sent a blue jay feather from camp. I sewed cloth bags for checkers, chess pieces, and Jenga blocks and hung them from the edge of the tables. I ironically tipped my hat to the genetic "hand we were dealt" and made bags for decks of cards as well. On each table, I included a hand-painted tag that said:

Post-Modern Home Entertainment Center
Requiring no batteries or plugs, merely two
People willing to sit face to face in play.
Always remember the importance of play.

For the next eight years, I painted furniture and sold it at art shows around the city, but I always was aware that I was an amateur as I had not formally studied art. When I referred to myself as an *untrained* artist, a couple of friends corrected me, "No, say you're *self-taught*."

My passion for flowers and gardening that had germinated when I worked at the restored farmhouse began to blossom again. I dove into planting my garden and didn't object to getting dirty fingernails, blisters on my hands, poison ivy, mosquito bites, or sore muscles. Plants like hellebores, crocuses, fragrant daphne, and edgeworthia chrysantha promised hope in winter, just like pansies with happy faces of purple, yellow, rose, and blue, and early daffodils heralded the coming of spring. I sprinkled fertilizer, spread pine bark and mushroom compost, divided plants, watered, and weeded. Early spring growth promised new life and beauty that made my insides quiver, almost like falling in love.

In her book, *A Garden of Fragrance*, Suzy Bales noted that flowers have been cultivated for thousands of years, even though they do not contribute to immediate nutritional needs. Rather, they fulfill our spiritual and aesthetic longings. Medieval gardeners believed that the perfume of flowers was God's breath on earth, and recent studies have shown that flowers are a *powerful positive emotion 'inducer.'* For example, in a 2005 study, Jeannette Haviland-Jones found that when people were given flowers, they felt more positive emotions than when they received gifts of candles or a fruit basket.

Flowers play an essential role in my emotional well-being. In my own erratic, highly textured life, I discovered that even placing a pansy and an ivy leaf in a tiny vase on the kitchen table provided a moment's joy in the doing and subsequent viewing, as does arranging fat, full hydrangea blossoms in a vase for the dining room table.

Very little makes me more exuberant than spotting the indomitable yellow bursts of daffodils emerge year after year from decaying leaves where I planted them thirty-years ago across the creek from our house. It is always a joy in mid to late-February to become aware that the first daffodils had bloomed, marking the arrival of spring and lifting my spirits once again.

I also find joy in painting bird feathers—ones I have collected on walks or been given by children—onto game tables and plant stands. Nature offers us many wonderful things and being one with them lifts my life.

In the months and years following my emergence from depression, the importance of the creative process revealed itself to me more profoundly than ever before. As a child, I somehow knew my life was better when I worked on creatively inspired projects because they were fun and made me feel good. As an adult, I saw that they are not only fun, but also life-giving, a vital part of the human spirit. Getting up from my living room sofa at the lowest point in my life, I came to understand the miracle of the creative process working in tandem with Shakespeare's affirmation that, "The readiness is all." *(Hamlet, V,ii, 234-237)*, that events will occur when they are destined to, and that we need to be prepared for anything. I'll never be able to explain what confluence of forces caused me to end up at my art cabinet that day. But I'm now convinced that creativity is sewn into our very fiber in varying colors, sheens, shapes, and textures. It is far more than a mere frill or entertainment. When we seek it out, it helps define us. Our gifts and passions vary drastically, and we each have to discover what they are and how to express them. Living a life of unexpressed talents can itself be cause for depression.

Looking back, I can see that I *chose* to engage in activities that enhanced my life and helped to elevate me above my anguish about our family disease. I also understand that I could so easily have made other choices that could have torn me down and immersed me in more misery. There is no doubt that, in the months and years after my family's diagnosis, the imaginative, creative process, like a trapeze artist's safety net, helped save my life.

I continued my work at the dining room table but knew I would need additional support for the long haul. From conversations with friends and various readings through the years, I was aware of the possible benefits of psychotherapy and decided to give it a try. I was fortunate to have the means and opportunity to do so. In May, when a time slot opened with Carole Light, the therapist that Sherry had recommended, I was eager to begin.

In our first meeting, I began describing our seven-year odyssey in search of a diagnosis for Hunter. I spoke matter-of-factly and unemotionally, simply telling our story. After several appointments, Carol asked how I could come in every week with so little emotion. I continued coming for a few more weeks, continuing to tell our story dispassionately. Gradually my trust in her grew, and then one day I told her about the schizophrenia diagnosis. My voice started getting louder; my words ran together; my face began to perspire. *"And six hundred dollars later she told me to go to two book stores, and if I found something good — let — her — know! Can you believe it?"*

"So, what did you do?" Carole blurted.

I slowed my breathing; it grew deeper and more deliberate. I was re-living the scene. I didn't respond. Carole grabbed a tennis racket from the corner.

"Here!" she insisted, *"Take this!* Kneel in front of the couch.

Hold it in both hands like this. Lift it over your head and slam it onto the cushion—like you're chopping wood!"

I positioned myself and silently swung the racket. How odd it felt.

"Say something!" Carole instructed.

"Ou!" I felt self-conscious.

"Come on!" Carole commanded.

I swung down hard on the sofa with a swoosh and a pop, then quickly raised it again.

"Hit it! Again! *Harder!"* she said.

I swung again and again. *Swoosh! Pop!* Growing up, we were never encouraged to express ourselves like this. People got silent in my family when they were angry, not violent.

"Good! *Say* her name!" she commanded.

"You bitch!" I yelled. I was beginning to get the hang of it.

"Yell! Again!—Louder!" she coaxed. "Like you're four—fighting with your brother!"

"He's not a schizophrenic!" I screamed. *"Let you know if I find something good? Big help you are!"*

"Good!" Carole coached. "Very good!"

"Why can't doctors say, *'I don't know?'*—I *hate* doctors!"

I hit the cushion again and again, harder, and yelled louder. I could feel my Southern upbringing—always holding back, being composed and mannerly—giving in to raw emotions and primal screams the likes of which I had not uttered since early childhood fights with my brothers. I slammed the tennis racket down again and again. I could hardly recognize the screams coming from myself. *"I hate that psychiatrist—I hate the way she treated us—I hate her cavalier attitude—I hate the first pediatric neurologist—I hate the disease—I hate it for my children—I hate it for myself—Our lives have been ruined."*

Breathless, I finally dropped the racquet and fell limply onto the couch. As I lay there, wiping perspiration and tears with my sleeve, trying to catch my breath, calm settled over me.

Weeks before, I had admitted to Carole that I felt I had been holding back most of my life. But from that day forward, like molten magma plying its way to the surface of the earth that is finally released in a volcanic eruption, the pressure of my rage and despair, once expressed, was greatly diminished.

Carole taught me many things, but the lesson that rises to the top is the realization that *for the rest of my life, from time to time, I will find myself riding the wave of sadness.*

Having spent part of almost every summer on the white sand beach of the Gulf of Mexico southeast of Mobile in Orange Beach, Alabama, I knew this metaphor by heart. There were times as a child riding a wave that I got tumbled and twisted and slammed against the bottom. With knees, elbows, and shoulders sometimes rubbed raw and bleeding, lungs out of air, nose full of water, I wasn't sure I would make it to shore alive. But never once did I fail to reach the safety of shore on my own.

After several months of gaining confidence in myself with individual therapy, Carole steered me into a co-ed therapy group that she led with her psychologist husband, Alex Redmountain. My disappointing experience with the Muscular Dystrophy Association group had left me unsure if a group of strangers who knew nothing about our disease would be helpful; but if I joined the group, I could teach them as I was doing with Hunter's doctors, teachers, and our family.

I took Dr. Harper's *big book* to the first meetings — no doubt to justify my being there. Perhaps I still equated asking for help with being weak. None of the members of the group knew of our disease, but, as it turned out, they had all learned to listen well. And I listened to *them*. Each week we asked for help or time or support or a simple check-in. As strange as it may seem, at first I found it difficult even to identify what I was feeling, let alone, know what I needed and ultimately ask for help. It was also challenging to learn how to respond to others without giving advice.

I learned from Alex another important life lesson: *More curiosity, less judgment.* In different words and at a different time, my mother in her infinite wisdom had counseled me to "ask people about themselves" and to understand that some people "just can't help it." Slowly I began to internalize this idea. Although admittedly I still sometimes lapse into spontaneous judgment, I became a better listener.

I now look back on those five years in this group as a transformation, a time of flowering in slow motion. I learned how to identify what was going on in my guts and heart. I made strides in asking for help, expressing anger, fear, joy, and love, all the while striving for brutal honesty in myself. Tears were integral to the process: releasing, cleansing, and learning to value and honor myself.

Around the time I joined the therapy group, I also started walking regularly with three friends. With Hunter and Ashby both in school all day, I had more time, and I had learned how important it was to take care of myself. I, who struggle with initiating anything, committed to making a plan, putting it on my calendar, and every Friday morning showing up to walk and talk and activate endorphins.

Walking through wooded neighborhoods for many years, we talked about brown rabbits, fledging blue birds, gardenias, the disturbing current and future water shortages in Atlanta, zoning issues, hydrangeas, fallen arches, children, presidential elections, Facebook, Egypt, parenting, disease, *my* disease, fear, love, and so much more.

One friend and I have now walked on Friday mornings for over twenty-five years. She has told stories of her daughters breaking records in NCAA Division III swim records at Williams College and graduating from law school; I have told stories of Hunter making a B on a high school exam and *passing* the course. And, with excitement, we applauded their respective accomplishments.

After five years in the weekly therapy group, I was ready to move on. Following an emotional farewell where I addressed everyone personally, I parted from them with sadness, knowing that I was at the end of another part of my journey. But I also felt excitement in my new-found strength. The time and money spent in that group proved without rival to be my best investment ever, producing dividends that altered my inner being forever in my quest for a meaningful life. This time when I took leave, I was smiling with anticipation rather than speeding along the highway filled with dread as I had after I had learned about our diagnoses.

Shortly before I said my farewells, one of the women who had already left the therapy group invited me to join her women's support group. She had spoken glowingly of this hallowed group after some of our sessions together with Carole and Alex. Having begun to rely on a weekly, structured routine, I cautiously agreed to give this new unknown group a try. I had become much more confident about exploring new relationships.

That was in 1993; our meetings arc still etched on all Wednesdays in my calendar. We bring our own lunch to a different person's house every week and sit at a dining room table. We take turns expressing what we need: "check in" or "time" or "an opportunity to whine or bitch." The subject may change every five minutes, we may tell stories more than once, and sometimes everyone is talking at one time, but always the agenda comes from our willingness to share our truths and listen well. We have discussed ourselves, all sorts of relationships, face lifts, abandonment, childhood trauma, Outward Bound, *New York Times* crossword puzzles, art, books, restaurants, poached salmon, doctor recommendations, grief, joy, depression, travel, death and dying, peonies, addiction, exercise, and, of course, myotonic dystrophy and CTG repeats. We have almost never failed to fill three hours, and we seldom miss a meeting unless we're sick or out-of-town. It is a luxury and a privilege, I know, to be able to devote this much time to supporting each other and nourishing ourselves in this way. We laugh and cry; we celebrate birthdays; we have spent weekends at a lake and coastal beaches. I have embraced the opportunity to tell my family stories from assorted angles, and after all these years, they know almost as much as I do about our disease.

I have listened to their stories, lived vicariously through *their* children's weddings and births of *their* grandchildren. Sometimes I feel a tinge of sadness, occasionally *deep* sadness, when I think of grandchildren, but those feelings eventually subside. I have had the opportunity to talk of disease and spring green in April and hellebore flowers in January, daffodils in February; I have read aloud letters and speeches that I have written. I have been loved, supported, encouraged, and accepted. I have come to believe that women have made it through the ages because of other women.

As I have learned to take better care of myself, I have found many ways to enjoy my life and other people. Twice a week I attend Hatha yoga classes where I routinely work on increasing my flexibility and strength, mastering the downward dog, tree, and pigeon positions, all the while inhaling and exhaling, oxygenating and stretching my muscles, expanding my belly, ending in Savasana and Namaste. About once a month I visit an antique market with my friend Esther and savor the cornucopia of eye candy for the visually inclined. Over the last few years, Larry and I have participated in organized walks with Country Walkers in Glacier Park, Montana, Newfoundland, Crete, New Zealand, and other places. I work at remembering the importance of play. One additional life-giving ingredient for me has been hosting an occasional dinner party with people I enjoy.

This new philosophy spilled over into other aspects of my life, like my marriage. When we had children, I had made a conscious choice to stay at home and not have an outside job; yet, during those early years as a mother, I often felt lonely and trapped. I had been searching for a meaningful purpose for my life, something bigger than and outside of myself. Meanwhile, Larry had been unabashedly charging full-steam ahead, embracing and rejoicing in his profession and volunteer pursuits — energy looking for a place to happen. I didn't have as much energy as he did and sometimes found his exuberance difficult to bear.

Several years after I had ended therapy, I read an article in the *New York Times Magazine*, in which the author advised: *Don't expect your husband to give you a life; and don't expect him to make you happy.* I had grown up with the belief that women should rely on their husbands for everything, including their happiness. It was one of those unspoken messages that girls, at least in my generation, absorbed through osmosis from parents, movies, and who knows what. Looking back, I can see that by now I was starting to be *in charge of my own happiness* and emerging as a capable, self-reliant woman who could take care of herself. Larry was entitled to go about his own life in his own way, but I didn't have to be an integral part of everything he did. When I read that article, it was an epiphany and a defining moment in my life and in our marriage.

Now I was ready to figure out what to do with my new-found strength and independence. What paths would beckon, which ones would I take?

8. Hunter's Story

After several changes in schools, as described in Part I, Hunter entered the transition program for students with learning disabilities as a fourth grader. As Hunter started the year, we noticed that it was becoming more and more difficult for him to get over his first daily hurdle of getting up and to the school bus stop by 7:20 A.M. Every morning he looked more tired than he did when he went to bed the night before. Years into this routine, he admitted that he slept on the bus to and from school every day. Like my mother, sleep was the most important thing in his life. To this day, he has never been able to awaken himself, even with the loudest alarm, clock radio, or under-the-pillow vibrator. Larry, who leaps cheerily out of bed every morning before his alarm sounds, figured how to live with our early morning sluggishness.

In spite of individual therapy and get-along groups, Hunter was sometimes treated unmercifully by other children and seldom defended himself. During a period in middle school, a couple of children frequently hid his gym shorts or shoes every day before class. Therefore, he arrived late to class, only to be reprimanded by the teacher in front of the other students. Finally, fellow students in the Transition Program stepped up and told the teacher what was happening.

Hunter continued along this steady course of struggling to get up, taking on the challenge of learning, and enduring harassment. But he never complained. He strove to be a good student and classmate. Except for the few bullies, everyone liked Hunter. Even though Hunter did not make a lot of friends, he talked about his classmates, especially those who were kind to him. It almost seemed that he did not recognize his shortcomings. It was just part of who he was, and he had decided not to let it ruin his life.

In tenth grade, possibly as an alternative for not having a group of friends to sit with, Hunter raced to the cafeteria to be first in line every day. One of his classmates told me as class would end, Hunter would drop his book bag and start sprinting across campus like Forrest Gump, only without the latter's athletic speed and agility. One day, as he raced toward the lunch room, his toe caught the edge of a sidewalk and—*thud*—he landed flat on his face. He managed to get himself up and, undeterred, resumed running.

"Hunter! Stop, man!" yelled a fellow Transition student who later described the incident to me. He asked, "Where are you going?" Hunter replied determinedly that he wanted to be first in line. Again, the boy told him, "Stop, Hunter, your face is all bloody."

"I put my hand on my face and—yuk! It was all bloody—and my braces were sticking out," Hunter later reported. "I couldn't close my mouth."

By this time, several classmates had gathered at the scene and insisted he go with them to the nurse's office. He and I spent the rest of the day at the emergency room and orthodontist's office. He had broken his nose. The gash on his nose required stitches and his braces a major overhaul. But Hunter was ready to go the next morning, not acknowledging how he looked. Again, he did not let this mishap deter him from participating in school.

We finally recognized that this "whatever" attitude was a part of myotonic dystrophy. Other symptoms of his disease also appeared or re-appeared on occasion, painful reminders of the challenges he would always face. He often complained that his waist hurt, probably a manifestation of slow motility and myotonia in his GI Tract caused by the disease. Sitting across from me at a restaurant one day, he started squirming on the edge of his seat. I noticed he had stopped breathing. "Hunter!" I yelled as I lunged toward him to perform the Heimlich maneuver. All of a sudden he vomited, slumped back into the booth, and sighed. My heart pounded as I recalled what I knew about choking and possible aspiration pneumonia in myotonic dystrophy. Fortunately, he was okay.

Occasionally, Larry and I heard him talking to himself alone in the next room. Did he create a fantasy world for survival? Did he hear voices? In his early years, he told us of an imaginary army that protected him. During high school, in his spare time, he wrote a book about a baseball player who probably epitomized the person that he wanted to be. Perhaps he was using his imaginary world to compensate for the life he could not have. Despite many challenges at school, Hunter complied with most rules. He raised no objections to wearing the school uniform, blazer and tie with shirttail tucked in. Although the ebb and flow of his life was far from smooth, he was never a depressed child, and he made steady progress in his academic work. However, he was aloof, naïve, and unaware of much of the world around him.

When Hunter was tested at the age of sixteen, his Rorschach test affirmed these patterns as described in the neuropsychological report:

> Hunter frequently misperceives the reality of situations in his environment. Hunter is defensively substituting fantasy for reality in stress situations. Hunter tends to avoid emotional responsiveness…is not comfortable around affective displays and fears psychological disruption and disorganization resulting from emotional breakthroughs.
>
> Hunter seems to be experiencing difficulties with interpersonal relationships. He does not manifest ordinary needs for closeness as do most adolescents, and he does not seem to have much curiosity or interest in people.
>
> Hunter seems to be setting high standards for himself that are beyond his functional capacity. Therefore, he feels disappointed and confused when he is not able to meet these goals.

The director of the Transition Program at Woodward Academy offered: *what gets Hunter in trouble [his aloofness] is also what saves him.* His general attitude of "whatever" protected him from feeling badly about his academic and social challenges, but it also meant that he often did not do the work, as he did not fear the consequences.

Happily, between bumpy places in the road, there were

stretches of unexpected smooth riding and even triumphs. Because they were rare, we celebrated his successes even more. One time when he was a sophomore, Hunter announced, totally out of the blue, that he was going to run for a class office. A student in the Transition Program was enraged when she overheard someone in the regular program making fun of him; she determined then and there to get him elected. She enlisted her friends to make campaign posters, taped them up in the well-travelled halls, and defying all odds, he was elected vice-president of his class!

The summer between his junior and senior years, Hunter went to Europe with a group of students from his school. He was "on fire" during this trip—taking pictures of everyone and every place they visited and learning about the history as well. It was reported by several of the students that Hunter became the group's walking encyclopedia. He has always been eager to help in any way that he can, and he applied those skills to the trip as well. For months after the trip, he told stories in great detail about his adventures in Europe.

Well into his senior year, Hunter announced that he wanted to be a pitcher on the varsity baseball team and was going to try out. He had not played baseball since age ten; and, during his last year in little league, when he was up at bat, he got hit by the pitcher and never swung at the ball again. Larry and I lovingly convinced him that it was highly unlikely he would make the team. But hating to see him disappointed, we suggested he inquire about a position as team manager. He talked to Tyler, a fellow Transition student, a highly energetic, affable fellow who was to be a co-captain of the baseball team. Tyler told him, "You're good in math. You could keep stats and stuff. I'll talk to Coach."

And so, he became team manager. He came home one afternoon crowing, "Coach Fritz wants me to go to Florida with the team!!" So, he accompanied the team to South Florida on a yellow school bus. Every night, while on their spring training he washed and delivered clean uniforms to the players' rooms. He beamed in his manager's uniform and relished being an integral part of the team—made possible by the power of small, nameless acts of kindness. His school went to the state play-offs that year but failed to win the championship. Nevertheless, it didn't matter to us; it was a winning year at our house. After dinner at the end-of-the-season team party at Tyler's house on a beautiful, flower-laden patio, the coach called Hunter to the front and quieted the crowd. He thanked Hunter, held up a plaque and read the inscription:

Hunter T. Lord is awarded Certificate of Merit
In recognition of high achievements
Team Manager
Varsity Baseball
1995

Through blurred vision, I saw several other mothers fingering away tears while a loud applause overpowered the riotous sounds of crickets as the sun slowly eased out of sight. The team members gave Hunter a school baseball jacket to keep and a plaque with scenes of players in action through the year, tangible evidence that in spite of his shortcomings and disabilities, he could still enjoy gifts of love and human decency. All of these years later, I still hug Tyler every time I see him.

At graduation in May of 1995, standing 6'4" and weighing 170 pounds with his once golden blonde hair now a dark brown, Hunter walked as proudly across that stage as the valedictorian who would go on to Harvard.

We still held onto the dream that he would go to college. After visiting several campuses, Hunter chose to attend Western Carolina University, a small university in North Carolina because it was rural and quiet, and he felt that he could manage the campus and small college town of Cullowhee. When he got to campus, Hunter joined a student group called Last Minute Productions. His skills at helping were useful as the group set up equipment and seating for spirit rallies and other school events. However, Hunter found the school work and managing his daily routine daunting. After he spent one semester over-sleeping and not understanding the accent of a foreign professor, the school invited him to take a semester off. Years later, he revealed that he often felt lonely at college, a rare acknowledgement of his feelings.

After he left college, Hunter spent five months working for a small computer company owned by one of Larry's acquaintances. He learned to up-grade computer hardware. Using a special miniscule screwdriver, he changed out motherboards and sister cards. Every day he lunched at the Waffle House next door and returned to work. The next summer he lived and worked at Camp Twin Lakes, a camp for children with serious illnesses and disabilities and other life challenges. He was promoted that summer from pot washer to dish washer. As expected, he sometimes showed up late only after someone went to awaken him. At summer's end, he began working in Larry's architectural office as a general administrative assistant. He continued taking computer courses at a local college until he came to me one day and said, "I don't think college is for everyone. It's not for me."

Here ended his college career. A bar chart (Veillette et al, 1986) that Dr. Harper included in his book (1989, p. 153) shows that over 60% of people with DM complete less than nine years of schooling; about 30% complete 9-13 years; and only about 3% complete more than 14 years. Hunter fit comfortably into the DM norm; in fact, he was in the top third.

Hunter continued working full-time in Larry's firm for more than fifteen years. He had more and less productive periods: sometimes he napped in his chair, even though he took Adderall to help keep him awake and focused. Without stimulant medication, I doubt that he would have been able to complete high school or to work at all.

For about a year and a half, Hunter drove a car until he had a couple of minor accidents and then totaled Larry's car on his way to work one morning. Shortly after that, he had a grand mal seizure and was required by law to stop driving for a year. Larry and I had always felt nervous about his driving and now questioned the prudence of allowing him to continue. We took him to a neuropsychologist for testing. Because of aloofness, slow mental processing, difficulty with visual-spatial processing and inability to multi-task, the doctor suggested he not drive again.

I drove him across town to the DMV at the Georgia State Patrol office where he signed a form agreeing to surrender his license willingly. Alarmed by the expression on my face on our way out, he tugged at my sleeve, "Mom! Mom! What's wrong?"

"It makes me sad that you're not able to enjoy a privilege that many, many adults do, through no fault of your own." Typically, uneasy with emotional expressions or psychological discussions, he said nothing more on the way to the car. He accepted this closed door with few questions.

Although he worked at Larry's office, Hunter spent an inordinate amount of time watching television and playing video games when he was home. Larry and I were exhausted from shouldering the responsibility for providing the motivation for him that we felt he needed. So, I called around and found a social group called *Just People*, a program for adults with developmental disabilities. Even though he was not developmentally disabled, we thought that the group might be a good fit for him.

Larry and I took him to the bowling alley for his first activity with the group. Several van loads of participants waited in the parking lot for others to arrive. They included those with Down syndrome, autism, ataxia, and other diagnoses we couldn't identify. Speechless with his eyes opened as wide as his typically opened mouth, Hunter gazed all around, exhibiting no emotion. One of the social liabilities of DM is that people have increasing difficulty showing facial expressions because muscle weakness often begins in the face and neck. Thus, we could not tell how he felt about being with this group. Some of the members politely introduced themselves. Finally, we asked Hunter if it was OK for us to leave. He nodded without even glancing our way.

We returned to the bowling alley a couple of hours later, just as the lights were dimmed for cosmic bowling, a funky, late 20th century invention. The music was blaring, the lights flashing, and, when the members weren't bowling, they were dancing and flailing their arms. They were the happiest group of people I had seen in a long time.

Hunter was talking to a pretty young counselor, but when he saw us he came rushing toward us. *"May I go to Six Flags with them on Sunday?!"*

Thus, began Hunter's happy five-year association with Just People. He filled albums with pictures from cruises to the Caribbean, Alaska, and Hawaii. His camera allowed him to be part of the group without having to talk. Within the context of Just People, he chose activities like Braves' games, Six Flags, and bowling. He liked the big events and often helped people who needed physical assistance, such as pushing their wheel chairs. He skipped social gatherings like pool parties where he would have to engage in idle chatter.

A family friend asked him after his first cruise, "What was your favorite part?" Without hesitation he answered, "That I paid for it myself."

Eventually, his energy waned and he could no longer handle night activities during the work week. And it took him progressively longer to recover after each cruise. He finally reached a point when he had to end his happy association with Just People.

Another activity Hunter enjoyed was golf. He bought himself a fine set of clubs and took private lessons in a golf shop near his office. He played for about 10 years, including golfing with members of our extended family during a reunion in 2000. He participated in golf tournaments at Larry's office to raise money for charities; and he and Larry often played together. Hunter always enjoyed the excitement of getting out on the course, whatever the occasion, no matter the score.

Sadly, even when Hunter was engaged in activities he enjoyed, evidence of his physical decline often rudely interrupted our lives. One Saturday when he was twenty-eight, Hunter and

Larry were headed home after eighteen holes of golf. Without any warning Hunter blurted, *"Pop, my heart is beating fast!"*

Larry pulled the car over and grabbed Hunter's wrist; he couldn't find a pulse. He tried different spots around his wrist. Still no pulse. He put his fingers on Hunter's neck and could feel the blood coursing rapidly. "Hunter, there's an emergency room just ahead! Do we need to turn in?"

Although the emergency room was full, when Larry mentioned the word *heart* he and Hunter were whisked into a small room and a medical team descended on him.

While this was happening, I was working in my garden without my cell phone. I casually returned the tools to the storage room, pulled off my gloves, and headed inside to discover a half dozen phone messages from Larry. I called him back. *"Did you tell them he has myotonic dystrophy?"*

"Yes, I did! But *I'm not sure I told them everything!"* he shouted.

I grabbed the big book off the shelf and sped to the hospital. When I arrived, I didn't see Larry, but there were the ER doctor and twelve orderlies and nurses around Hunter's bed. One was talking on the phone to a cardiologist, trying to determine which medication to give Hunter next since the first one had not brought his heart rate down from 250 beats per minute. Since a normal rate is between 60-100 beats, there was mild panic among those surrounding Hunter. His EKG looked like a toddler scribbling. He was experiencing ventricular tachycardia, a symptom often found in people with myotonic dystrophy, and the second leading cause of sudden death of those with DM.

I finally spotted Larry insistently telling the medical group about the risks of treating a patient with myotonic dystrophy, especially if a muscle relaxer were required. With his physical size and booming voice, I can imagine how he must have appeared to the medical staff as he wrestled with his deepest fear.

The first medication did not slow down the heart, but with the second medication, Hunter's heart rate slowly dropped to around 100 beats. Hunter was released on the second day, and we scheduled an appointment with his regular cardiologist the next. As soon as the cardiologist reviewed the report from the hospital, he immediately scheduled for combination pace-maker/ defibrillator (an Implantable Cardiac Defibrillator, or ICD) surgically implanted in Hunter's chest. By day's end, Hunter was a bionic man.

With my curiosity in overdrive most of the time, I later asked this seasoned cardiologist if Hunter's grand mal seizure several years earlier could have been caused by a similar cardiac event. He responded, "Yes, it certainly could have."

Since then, manifestations of DM have continued to intrude on Hunter's life. Hunter has been to the emergency room with an impacted colon and now takes Miralax to try to preempt other GI blockage emergencies.

When Hunter was about 25, he complained that he could not see the golf ball without raising his head. We had observed that his eyelids were beginning to lose their strength so it was off to another specialist who implanted adjustable silicone slings in his eyelids that connect to his forehead muscles so that he can elevate the eyelids and hold them open and be able to see.

After he had fallen several times, Hunter began wearing hiking boots to support his weak ankles and lower legs, but when he was 34, his ankle gave way as he descended a flight of steps and he fell head-first into a sheetrock wall and knocked a six-inch hole in it with his head. He could have easily broken his neck but fortunately he hit the sheetrock between the wooden studs. After that event, he has worn air casts to provide additional support for his ankles.

Although Hunter has difficulties, limitations, and a streak of stubbornness, he is good-natured almost all the time. If he feels comfortable around someone, he will look him in the eye and converse, whereas, if he doesn't get good vibes he will not make eye contact.

For a number of years, Larry's office was Hunter's comfort zone and his community. His regular responsibilities included de-livering the mail, with alarms on his watch to remind him when to go to the post office, and re-ordering supplies for the office. But around age twenty-eight, something in his brain seemed to mature, and he evolved into the Event Planner. He began or-ganizing the in-house golf tournaments twice a year. After the tournaments, he invited all participants and significant others for dinner and handed out cash prizes at Manuel's Tavern, a local restaurant. He created brackets for March Madness, the college basketball tournament at the end of the season, and a large group of people joined in betting on the outcome to win "the pot." Hunter also arranged Christmas-tree decorating contests to raise money for battered women's shelters.

He initiated and participated in Halloween costume contests. Halloween was his favorite holiday as he reveled in planning and creating his own costume. The first year he sewed his own Super Girl costume. He watched me sew one line of stitching with the sewing machine and took it from there: red skirt, red cape, platinum blonde wig and blue top into which he figured a way to sew in foam breasts.

Hunter became a minor philanthropist, offering financial support to office mates walking in the Susan G. Komen 3-Day Breast Cancer Walk and other non-profit events. He was a generous supporter and sponsor for an annual fundraising event for Camp Twin Lakes. He organized office bake sales to raise money for myotonic dystrophy research. In 2011, he raised $1,000 to contribute to the development of the camp's new farm that was established to serve as a demonstration and learning site for the campers and to provide some of the food for camp. Much to our surprise and delight, several months after his donation, a hand-carved wooden sign was erected naming part of the farm, *Hunter's Garden*. Most of Hunter's events involved organizing lists and activities that were geared toward fundraising; an activity where he could utilize his uncanny understanding of math that exceeds the formal education he has completed. In his own way, he was a real success.

Over time the effects of the myotonic dystrophy became more debilitating. The firm's office manager and the director of operations observed that Hunter was having more trouble meeting his responsibilities and shared his concerns with Larry. Larry realized Hunter could no longer sustain the energy necessary to work eight hours a day, and everyone decided that Hunter should cut back on his hours. Fortunately, Lord, Aeck & Sargent had a very good disability policy, and in 2010 Hunter was able to go on to disability, allowing him to work 16 hours a week with the insurance company paying the remainder of his wages.

About this same time, after nearly thirty years of running his own firm, Larry was approaching seventy, and he began making plans to turn the firm over to the next generation. He spent a little time deciding what he wanted to do next, and contemplated continuing with the firm in a role of advisor or mentor. Then he was recruited by a large architectural firm and was excited by the new challenges that this opportunity offered. But as with many things in life, *you can't tell a book by looking at the cover.* He soon found that, unlike his own firm, the culture of his new firm was competitive and not conducive to collaboration and "rallying the troops" to which he was accustomed. Thus, his involvement was short lived. However, as the word got out that Larry had "retired", he started getting requests to consult with different architecture and engineering firms on their business and marketing plans.

With every strand of his once-blonde hair now silver and tiring more easily than he used to, Larry still possesses the motor that never stops, but now occasionally sputters. He has always been interested in helping others, particularly supporting organizations empowering youth like Camp Twin Lakes, the YMCA, Concorde Fire Soccer Club, and, most recently, EARTH University in Costa Rica. He valued all these projects, but perhaps Larry's most important contribution has been to Camp Twin Lakes where he has served on the board since 1989 when the camp was a mere kernel of an idea that Doug Hertz, a friend of Larry's, imagined. Doug wanted to create a place where children with serious illnesses, disabilities, and other life challenges could have a great camp experience. He decided that Larry was "the most childlike architect" he knew and asked that he and his firm Lord, Aeck, & Sargent design the physical facility. The camp officially opened in 1993 and now serves over 5,000 children each year.

Larry has worked with them for more than twenty years and continues to manage all their capital projects. I have great admiration for all that Larry has done to help young people.

A couple of months after Larry's departure from Lord, Aeck & Sargent in December of 2011, it seemed appropriate for Hunter, now age 35, to leave as well. The effect of the disease continued apace with progressive muscle weakness, excessive day-time sleepiness, leg, back, and abdominal pain. His resignation coincided with the annual 2012 State of the Firm meeting; and at the end of a full day of introductions of new employees, presentations, and strategic plans, the moderator announced that there was one *special* report from the firm's newsroom. Up walked Jackson Kane, an architect Larry and I had first known as a teenager thirty years ago, one whom Larry had supported and mentored through the years and a person who had known Hunter since he was five.

Jackson began under the guise of a reporter. And behind him loomed a large screen projecting a power point photomontage of Hunter set to the theme of the Mary Tyler Moore Show.

"Good evening. We are bringing you stunning news today from the world of business. Hunter Lord (headshot of Hunter) has announced that he is leaving Lord, Aeck, and Sargent, the architecture firm he helped to found (image of Larry and his two partners with Hunter photoshopped over Larry). Hunter has been with the firm for over twenty-years—full time for more than fifteen of them—and though the most conspicuous part of his job might have been that of mail carrier, to those of us who worked with him, he was so much more.

"Hunter was something of a town crier (image of Cliff Clavin,

the mailman from Cheers), reporting the latest news of the day
along with occasionally useful trivia. He was an avid sports fan
(image Harry Caray, late baseball announcer for the Chicago
Cubs), and could give you the play by play from last night's game
in lurid detail and, come September, recite from memory every
conceivable path that might lead his beloved Atlanta Braves to
the playoffs this year (image of Sid Bream, a player who scored
the winning run with a dramatic slide at home to advance the
Braves to the World Series), no matter how unlikely. But Hunter's
interests went beyond sports: he was a close observer of the stock
market (image of Jim Cramer) and could embarrass you, without
gloating, by the performance of his 401k relative to yours (image
of Warren Buffett, American business magnate, philanthropist and
one of the most successful investors in the world). If you were having a baby (image of pregnant woman at office) you could send an
all-staff e-mail to announce the blessed event, or you could just tell
Hunter and there would be an office pool by the end of the day.
And it wasn't just babies, either: March Madness (image of Barack
Obama with basketball bracket), the Super Bowl (image of Super
Bowl), and the LAS golf tournament (image of golf tournament).
If you could organize a pool of people to wager on the outcome of
an event, Hunter would, which made him more than just our office
reporter; it made him our bookie. And just like our friend Charlie
Hustle, Hunter didn't let the fact that he was participating in an
event prevent him from laying a friendly bet of his own (image of
Pete Rose, famous baseball player with nickname of Charlie Hustle and later manager who was banned from baseball for betting on
games his teams were playing when he was manager).

   "Hunter is leaving us today for Camp Twin Lakes (image of

Camp Twin Lakes), a network of camps that provides life-changing experiences to thousands of children with serious illnesses,
disabilities, and other challenges each year. And while Hunter
says he isn't exactly sure what he will be doing when he gets there,
you can bet that his job description will include this: role model
(image of Charles Barkley, all-star professional basketball player).
That's because in addition to everything else that Hunter does to
make our office run more smoothly and to brighten our workday,
he also quietly, cheerfully, relentlessly, and resiliently demonstrates
every day that you can live with a chronic illness and not let it
define you; that you can overcome adversity by doing something
about it, that you can spread hope to others, one bake sale at a
time. And for that, he is much more than a mild-mannered reporter; (image of Christopher Reeve, the actor famous for playing
Superman) he is our *hero*. (Image of Hunter in his Supergirl
costume with Superman theme now playing while Hunter was
invited to come up to receive a plaque).

As Hunter went to the front of the room, there was a long
and heartfelt standing ovation with hardly a dry eye in the room.
After this wonderful send-off, Hunter took the weekend off
and on the following Monday began working part-time as general office support for the camp he loves. Hunter continues to
work for the camp four hours a day as an administrative assistant
with fundraising duties. He often organizes bake sales to support
Hunter's Garden, soliciting donations from family and friends
and inviting them to participate as sponsors. He raises more than
$3,000 a year and makes a substantial contribution from his own
money as well. Interestingly, Hunter is not concerned with his

financial situation but, in fact, is delighted to continue to get paid so he can contribute to others.

Larry and I long ago adjusted our expectations to correspond with who Hunter is. Most of the time we're able to tune out the constant drone of television and video games, allow him to sleep until after noon on weekends, and go about our lives. Often friends talk about their own children, their colleges — some Ivy League — semesters in Spain, backpacking in New Zealand, trailers for their films on YouTube, hat designing in Beijing, internships in New York and San Francisco, and their grandchildren. I occasionally feel sad that our children have not and will not ever enjoy these types of experiences and successes.

I look at Hunter, tall, bright in many ways, so full of potential, and I sometimes wonder *what if…* But we are grateful that he has his own interests, his own passions, and his own way of creating a life that matters. He lives with graceful acceptance of his life, using his abilities rather than being constrained by the effects of his disease. He has a wide range of hobbies and interests. All we have to do is to ask a question about a particular fact and, drawing on the many hours he has watched the *History Channel* and *Nature*, Hunter can give a history of a particular king or queen or explain the behavior of a specific animal. Reflecting his mathematical skills, he went through a period of assembling complex 3-D puzzles, including a six-foot tall grandfather clock. He became interested in Sudoku where he could beat the most difficult of the puzzles. He loves to read, especially books in a series, like the Harry Potter collection. And he's an avid Atlanta Braves' fan with a collection of 94 and ever growing number of autographed baseballs. His leadership in organizing March Madness brackets and betting pools continues to grow. Last year, he talked over 100 people into putting in their five dollars, with the top three taking home the winnings distributed in a manner only Hunter understands. The person with the worst results gets their five dollars back.

He enjoys traveling and, in the past, accompanied Larry and me on some of our Country Walker tours in Europe and New Zealand. Unfortunately, he no longer can manage the long hikes for these trips, but he still travels with us to various places. He loves family events such as weddings and reunions and faithfully attends them all. He likes to teach relatives how to play games or learn new games from them—and is delighted when he unfailingly wins. Although he can no longer do many sports such as hiking and golf, he sometimes swims at the local YMCA. He lives with graceful acceptance of who he is.

One of Hunter's quirks is his reluctance to part with anything. During his high school trip to France and Italy he washed his favorite Pirates Cove T-shirt. It came from a restaurant we frequented by boat in the summer in Josephine, Alabama. It was Hunter's kind of place: "No shoes, no shirt, no problem!" He hung the shirt on the balcony outside his room in France, but during the night, it blew away. The next morning when Hunter discovered it missing, he reportedly raced down the steps, searched the alley until he found it, and carefully brought it back upstairs. Now, worn thin and frayed at the edges, this favorite, well-traveled shirt still occupies a place in his dresser along with a passel of others in similar condition.

He never throws anything away. He keeps empty toothpaste tubes and used movie stubs. He rolls red Baby Bonne Bell wax coverings into balls and stores them in a kitchen drawer. I often wonder if this quirky behavior is a throwback to my great aunt who collected bits of string from everywhere and kept her collection on a table.

Hunter's accepting "whatever" attitude about his life and limitations was always perplexing, but recently we learned about a possible explanation. During a neurologist's presentation at IDMC-8 (The Eighth Meeting of the International Myotonic Dystrophy Consortium held in Clearwater, Florida in 2012), I was delighted to learn a new word: *anosognosia,* a condition defined as "a lack of awareness of impairment, not knowing that a deficit or illness exists." The term is derived from three Greek word stems, "a" meaning *without,* "nosos" referring to *disease* and "gnosos" meaning *knowledge.* As first described by Francois Babinski, a French neurologist in 1914, it is caused by actual brain cell changes in the pre-frontal lobes that lead to a lack of self-awareness and may affect memory, other cognitive skills, emotions, or physical movement.

In other words, anosognosia is a physiological condition in which a person suffering from a disability, even a severe one like paralysis or total blindness, is unaware of his or her disability. It differs from denial, a psychological defense mechanism that leads people to consciously or unconsciously suppress their feelings. In the case of anosognosia, individuals are truly unaware of their conditions. Although it can alleviate suffering from an impairment, it also can lead to dire consequences when, for example, the patient does not adhere to doctors' instructions or take medications as prescribed.

Whether or not Hunter has this neurological condition, the

definition aptly describes his lack of anxiety and anticipation. Hunter's *unawareness, aloofness, naïveté,* and *lack of concern* about things is striking. For example, he takes large bites of food even though they frequently cause him to choke. He still relies on Larry, and especially me, to structure his life: schedule doctors' appointments, transport him, re-order prescriptions, and make sure he eats nutritious food. In general, we need to provide 24-hour support for him because he does not see what needs to be done and cannot be responsible for doing things like getting up and taking his medications. Remarkably, whether getting a shot as a child and looking at the injection as administered, going through the implantation of his defibrillator or eye slings, receiving shocks from his cardiac device when his pulse is over 200, he is usually cooperative and cheerful and seemingly unafraid. For Hunter—as well as Larry and me—this neurological condition is a gift.

Hunter has lived an extraordinary life. He has many limitations, but he has transcended them in remarkable ways. Through his passion for helping people and for raising money for worthy causes, he has created a strong and supportive community of friends and colleagues. We celebrate the fact that Hunter has an exuberance for life. He is liked by everyone, and Hunter likes most everyone. Through his love of sports and videogames, he has on-line friends around the world. He has a sense of purpose and works hard to meet his goals. He is the CEO of his own life.

9. Ashby's Story

Unlike his older brother, Ashby was acutely aware of his genetic inheritance and terrified of its consequences. As an adolescent and young adult, his extreme anxiety led him to self-medicate, using a wide variety of street drugs. His quest to *"just be normal"* drove him to distance himself from our middle-class expectations of education and career and throw himself into precarious situations, illegal activities, and homelessness where he felt accepted and successful—free of our goals that had proved to be frustratingly elusive. While he shared Hunter's lethargy and need for a lot of sleep, Ashby was also impulsive and often careened from disaster to disaster. He required a completely different type of parenting. Ashby was often far removed from us both physically and emotionally, sometimes by his own volition and other times at our insistence. We were aware of Ashby's physical manifestations of DM, but his perplexing and frightening behavior was our primary concern.

Even before Ashby was officially diagnosed with DM, he was struggling in school. When he was in second grade, a graduate student in psychology administered a test to Ashby's class for her study on gender differences in stress coping skills in school-aged children. Ashby's test results revealed low scores in emotional health (because of his high anxiety), social ease, and especially study skills. The graduate student noted that, if Ashby couldn't cope, he would try to please others at a cost to himself; or he would placate or withdraw. When Ashby listened to me read this portion aloud, he recognized his words and said, "I manipulated my own mind."

Midway through second grade, Ashby took a series of psychological tests, and the examiner reported the following:

> "An absolute delight to work with…seemed aware of his learning differences…questioned why [reading] has been such a slow process…very easily distracted…not "tuned in…experiencing anxieties about his performance, [which] …was not unexpected given that he was a highly motivated child who was not able to achieve, even with a great deal of extra effort…"

Throughout his elementary and secondary education, reports from teachers divulged similar symptoms in Ashby: "Teases peers, misunderstands class work, cannot organize himself, has difficulty getting work started, and turns work in late." They also noted that he *worried* a lot, was overly sensitive to criticism, and was bothered by his brother. These last comments reflected feelings he often expressed at home. On top of his struggles in school, Ashby was embarrassed by how Hunter looked and acted and, when he was around his friends, Ashby hated having Hunter there. He often announced to Larry and me, "Hunter is a hard brother to have."

As a result of the tests and recommendations from the psychologist and his teachers, we enrolled Ashby in a special school. He spent grades 3-5 in two different schools for children with learning disabilities. Hunter had followed the same route but managed his academics much better, so we hoped that these interventions would work for Ashby as well. However, the struggles continued. At the first of these schools, Ashby's teacher consistently assigned the same kind of homework with little variety and creativity woven into the curriculum—an injustice to a creative and active child. Ashby became obsessed with an annoying student who followed him around, copied him, and nearly drove him to the brink. He told us frequently that he hated school; it was boring. One day, a couple of months after he had started in the school, he proclaimed, "I liked the way this school looked—but it *doesn't feel good.*"

The next year, when he was in fourth grade, we moved him to another school for children with learning disabilities but with a different philosophy. His new teacher provided positive reinforcement and encouraged creativity. Every good deed by any student earned a marble in a jar. When it was full, the class was rewarded with a party. With the Orton-Gillingham approach, Ashby learned phonics and soon was able to sound out every word placed before him; but he complained that when he read paragraphs, the words went into his head and didn't make sense. He was extremely distracted by noises. He remembers hearing construction workers outside his classroom at one point and how the sound made it impossible for him to focus on the meaning of words. Like a butterfly, he would alight briefly on a book or task before taking flight again, never fully engaging in the subject at hand and seldom completing an assignment.

His test results through his elementary and secondary years consistently mentioned auditory and visual processing problems; difficulties with memory, organization, written directions, and time management. He was not over-active but easily distracted—not tuned in. He was also impulsive, stressed, and anxious about his learning differences, especially in math and reading. It was as if his young, innocent brain had been randomly riddled with buckshot. In fifth grade, the pediatrician prescribed Ritalin to help him focus. It helped him to concentrate some, but it did not solve all his problems.

As Ashby's struggles with school continued, Larry and I shifted our frustrations, our questions, and our attitude when we learned the lesson from one of his counselors, *the root of all conflict is unmet expectations*. Instead of trying to "fix" Ashby, we began asking, "What are appropriate expectations for Ashby with all his strengths and weaknesses?"

After three years in special schools with 8-10 students in a class, Ashby moved to a small, private school in sixth grade, even though he still lagged in reading. He desperately needed a larger social setting but would continue to receive individualized attention—or so we were told.

In his new school, Ashby started the year working conscientiously as he always did. But soon the challenges faced him. He recalled vividly the first day of science class when students were asked to recite Newton's Law and the definition of the *scientific method*. He had no clue. He had a brand new *seventh* grade science book his teacher had ordered for her *sixth* graders. It included physics and equations, and he didn't know what they were. He didn't understand much of the vocabulary. In other words, before he started the year, he was already way behind. Nevertheless, he worked diligently on his science project, in which he constructed a three-dimensional cell. It was a creative, hands-on assignment where he excelled. He turned it in proudly.

"You have not followed the *scientific method*—which," the teacher reminded him, "you studied in science class all of last year."

"But, remember, I was at another school. I haven't had science since the second grade. We put celery in a jar with food coloring and watched it turn blue. What is the *scientific method*, anyway?"

Despite his effort and his lack of background, the teacher gave him a "D" on this project. By this point, Ashby was utterly defeated and had begun to slack off. For the rest of his schooling, Ashby would usually start the year with good intentions, but by six weeks, he had given up, and the calls from teachers would begin. Initially the teachers called to express their concerns about Ashby's academic struggles, but then, as Ashby became frustrated, they would call to talk about his behavioral issues.

Happily, he did have occasionally positive experiences. One day in eighth grade he said out of the blue, "You won't believe what my favorite subject is this year." I had no idea.

"*English. I love* literature; I just don't like to read."

Robert Long, his highly energetic eighth grade English teacher captivated not only Ashby, but all students regardless of their standing in the class, by acting out almost everything he taught—Shakespeare, Faulkner, whoever. I had known the teacher when he was a child, the first boy I knew with a pierced ear. His mother often threw her arms in the air in desperation. What *else* could she possibly do to help him focus and comply?

At their wits' end, his parents sent him off to boarding school in eighth grade, the same grade he now chose to teach. In the interim he had finally graduated from high school and—amazingly—college. I wondered if his choice to teach adolescents was a self-imposed obligation to serve youth the same age he was when he began facing his biggest challenges. He was by far the best teacher Ashby ever had throughout his schooling and no doubt touched the lives of all the students he taught. Sadly, after three years, perhaps feeling that he had "served his time," this gifted teacher headed off to law school at Stanford.

Unfortunately, not many of Ashby's teachers were able to reach Ashby as Robert had. We continued to watch him struggle in most of his classes, and, when he was in eighth grade, we decided to have him tested by the same psychologist who had seen him in the second grade. Six years after these earlier assessments, the academic challenges had increased, and the gap between expectations and Ashby's capabilities had widened. The results revealed that Ashby now had difficulty listening and determining what information was important and therefore struggled with note-taking during lectures; he had trouble with reading comprehension, writing research papers, and organizing his work; his thought processes were disorganized and slow. His fingernails bitten to the quick were a reminder of his constant anxiety.

In contrast to his struggles at school, Ashby found success playing soccer from age nine through high school. Still, in spite of his good coordination and general athletic ability, coaches sometimes reprimanded him, "You're not doing your best—you could've run the mile faster." Coulda, shoulda, woulda.

I often wondered if he would do better if he became a goal-

ie so he wouldn't have to run up and down the field for an entire game. I discovered a little poem he had written years earlier:
"Playing soccer is really fun, just as long as I don't have to run."
Again we asked ourselves, what were appropriate expectations for
him *on the soccer field?* Despite occasional comments from coaches
about his effort, he mostly achieved positive feedback and satisfaction from the game.

Throughout his schooling, Ashby had difficulty getting up in
the mornings and displayed less and less motivation as the school
year progressed. Like Hunter, he was content to watch TV or play
Nintendo for endless hours. A quote from Dr. Harper's big book
had struck me with amazing familiarity the first time I read it:
*"We have found that affected individuals, when just mildly incapaci-
tated, were often content to sit or lie idly for hours," (Caughey, 1963,
cited in Harper, 1989, p. 153).*

This one behavior alone is a phenomenon nearly impossible
for others to comprehend, much less accept. Even close family
members, including me, struggle to tolerate this symptom even
though we know it is an integral part of the disease, not willful
laziness. Over the years, I have grown to believe that there are few
people who choose to be lazy and avoid daily tasks and activities
normally expected of people. The majority of us don't *choose* to
wake up every morning with the purpose of failing to complete
our work and making others angry. In my view, there is generally
an invisible cause that prevents them from living up to others' expectations. Dr. Melvyn Levine contends in his book *The Myth of
Laziness* that there is *always* some physical aberration underlying
lazy behavior. There are diseases that are described as *lazy diseases*

like mononucleosis and hookworm. Should myotonic dystrophy be included on this list?

That same year, Ashby wrote the following poem for an English assignment that showed us how he perceived his abilities and challenges:

Ashby
Athletic, artistic, animated, and agile,
Son of Shannon and Larry Lord,
Lover of family, friends and pets,
Who feels anxious before tests, scared in pitch-black dark, and ecstatic
When summer comes,
Who needs time management, more energy, and balanced chi,
Who gives a helping hand, sympathy, and love,
Who fears failure, being buried alive, and silence,
Who would like to see Ampsterdan [sic], Jamaica, and The Virgin Islands,
Resident of the woods on Mt. Paran Rd.,
Lord.

If only we had known how to embrace and build on what he clearly knew about himself as a budding adolescent. But, at the time, we had no clue, and no one who worked with Ashby seemed to know either.

With hindsight, I am not surprised that the first weekend after Ashby was re-tested, a new and bigger problem hit us. That Sunday afternoon, just after Larry finished refereeing a soccer match, the father of a younger student at Ashby's school informed him that Ashby had shown his son a bag of marijuana in the bathroom at school on Friday. Larry was shocked and called me. After he returned home, Larry and I held Ashby hostage in our living room for over two hours until he finally confessed. Ashby described the situation as "another student brought the stuff to campus and had talked me into using and dealing it." We knew we were on a slippery slope but we decided to report it to the school. Larry called the Head of School at home on a Sunday afternoon to report the incident on school property the Friday before. She gasped over the phone. "This could mean *expulsion* you know!"

"We know," Larry said, "but he will have to face the consequences."

Monday morning, Ashby and I met with the middle school principal. Once again, I found myself as the lone parent in another nerve-wracking conference. Regrettably, Larry was often out-of-town or unavailable when meetings were called on short notice. I crossed my legs multiple times trying to get comfortable, finally accepting there was no comfort to be found in such circumstances. The eighth grader who had brought the marijuana to campus was expelled. Ashby was suspended for two weeks.

For those couple of weeks, while Ashby was suspended, I was tethered at home with Ashby. He sat at the kitchen table doing homework for much of the time and spent the rest of the time on his skate board. Through the kitchen window I watched with trepidation as he heedlessly attempted dangerous tricks on his skate board, seemingly undaunted about the possibility of any physical injury. He usually returned with a scowl, a limp, or bloody knees and elbows.

We wanted to act quickly as we were sure that Ashby was already using marijuana. From this new vantage point, we looked back on some of his disturbing behavior and realized that his marijuana use might have been the root cause. I immediately found the name of a highly-recommended drug counselor, and Ashby started attending a counseling group for teens with drug problems. So Ashby began, without much resistance, seeing the first of what would turn out to be a long list of "counselors" that we hoped would straighten him out. Despite the initial fallout, Larry and I were relieved that, as we believed at the time, we had caught his use of marijuana early enough. At the same time, we were in a state of constant disbelief that we had to deal with such issues in the first place. As teenagers, we had both walked a rather straight line and respected rules and laws from childhood on. But teaching by example bore no relevance here.

For the rest of Ashby's high school career, I stayed up weekend nights reading in the living room until Ashby got home. We always chatted before he went to bed, and I never detected anything unusual. Thus, it came as complete surprise that mid-way through the eleventh grade, his drug use surfaced again. I simply couldn't believe it.

In the course of several conversations with school officials, we learned that the road behind the high school campus was called "Cocaine Lane" by the kids, and that they suspected that Ashby was selling drugs. We found out later he stored them in a hidden compartment in the trunk of his car. Although they were suspicious, the school officials never actually caught him in the act, so he was not suspended or expelled. Because of these continuing concerns, Ashby resumed going to the same drug counselor as before. However, as we later learned, the kids who came to the counseling group would go out right after the session was over and smoke a joint together.

We gave Ashby periodic drug tests and took away his car for weeks when tests came back positive. We felt confident that, eventually, he would learn from these consequences. But consequences and cause and effect relationships never seemed to matter to him. Perhaps to find an excuse for his using, I began to wonder if the myotonic dystrophy was contributing to his inability to change his ways.

Still, Larry and I remained optimistic, and, with each new plan or consequence, we believed that this effort, at last, would be *the fix*. I continued trying to motivate Ashby to do his school work. A math tutor came to the house once a week during high school. I made sure he completed his other school work: I read some assignments aloud; later we borrowed tapes and a tape recorder from the Library for the Blind so he could listen to books on tape. But he played them at top speed so the words were incomprehensible. Either he was not interested, or more likely, overwhelmed and defeated by the learning gap between himself and the other students.

Often complaining, Ashby generally adhered to his curfew. However, he began using cologne to mask a musty odor of marijuana in his clothing. It lurked as a constant reminder every time we passed. He avoided Larry and me as he grew more sullen and distant. Our house, in which I had invested so much of myself, my peaceful sanctuary tucked far from the road in the woods, our mountain house 20 minutes from downtown Atlanta, felt as if it had been invaded and defiled. I was constantly on edge in my own home.

In retrospect, I realize that what Larry and I took for defiance may have been Ashby's attempt to self-medicate in order to live with his extreme anxiety and sense of failure. Many years later, I met a California woman at a DM conference. Her 38-year-old son with DM had a marijuana dependency, and she told me that she had finally concluded that "smoking pot is the only time my son experiences any relief from anxiety."

Was that also true for Ashby?

Larry and I often asked ourselves, what part of his behavior was a manifestation of the DM gene, what part a psychological reaction to his awareness that he had a degenerative disease, and what part was just being a typical adolescent? We had no idea where we were headed from here. But by now we knew our lives were no longer following an orderly, predictable pattern.

In April 2000, spring of his senior year, Ashby, Larry, and I were planning to go to a family orientation at the small, liberal arts college in North Carolina where Ashby had applied and been accepted. Larry had been very involved in the college admission process, videotaping Ashby playing soccer and sending the tapes to coaches at different colleges. But down deep I knew he was not ready for college. He was wrestling with marijuana dependency and a string of learning, attention, and behavioral issues. It had taken my constant daily guidance and discipline for him to manage school so far; how could he possibly handle college on his own? At the same time, I was willing to give him a chance to try being a college student, but I could not in good conscience go to the orientation and feign enthusiasm. So, Larry and Ashby headed off without me.

Unfortunately, my intuition about Ashby and college proved

correct. During his first weeks there, he was practicing soccer three-hours a day, staying up late, smoking cigarettes and marijuana, drinking alcohol, and over-sleeping. He never got his computer working, missed half his classes, and didn't turn in assignments. His conscientious roommate moved out after the first week. After seven weeks, Larry drove to North Carolina for parents' weekend. While there he found that Ashby was not playing in any of the soccer games. When he visited with some of Ashby's teachers, Larry discovered that Ashby was failing most of his classes. Larry suspected that marijuana was a major contributor and demanded that Ashby give him a urine sample. The urine was tested in Atlanta, and the results showed a very high level of THC. Larry called Ashby and told him to start packing and be ready to return home. Larry knew one of the administrators of the college and arranged for Ashby to withdraw for "medical reasons" to avoid having an expulsion on his record. We later learned that, when he had first gone to college, he had taken a sports bag filled with marijuana to use and to sell.

Every day for three weeks after his return to Atlanta, Ashby slept until mid-afternoon then flopped on the sofa to watch television for the rest of the day. We put him through several tests, including a sleep test. But we already knew that sleepiness and low motivation are often symptoms of myotonic dystrophy, marijuana use, and depression. Whatever the mix, it rendered him almost non-functioning. At our insistence, Ashby enrolled in a 3-month, part-time, out-patient program at a local drug rehab center. Ashby, as usual, talked a good game, often convincing experienced drug counselors that he had stopped using, when, in reality, this was not true.

One day, I asked a counselor if he thought myotonic dystrophy could be intertwined with Ashby's addiction.

"Ashby is dealing with the *disease of addiction*, and only that!" he said emphatically.

"Yes, but myotonic dystrophy can affect most organs and systems, including the brain," I retorted. "I am sure the disease contributes in some way."

"He is dealing with the disease of *addiction*—*that* and only *that*! *Period*!" he snapped.

My blood began to boil, but I knew, from previous failed attempts to convince doctors and counselors, that arguing with this man would lead me nowhere. Still, it seemed plausible, even probable, to me that Ashby's symptoms of DM and addiction were inextricably bound.

After Ashby completed the drug program, Larry and I pressed him to find a job. He finally landed one at a soccer store, but it closed a month later. He was fired from his next job for routine tardiness. Once again, he assumed his do-nothing pattern. His lethargy and lack of motivation, his stepped-up use of cologne, and his recalcitrant attitude hung in our house like a toxic cloud on a hot summer day. I found myself now snapping at my family for insignificant things. In February 2001, Larry and I reached our limit. After much hand-wringing and discussion about the situation, we told Ashby he had to move out. We would pay his rent, but he'd have to work to cover all other expenses. He found a place with some friends and moved out.

We stayed in occasional touch and knew that after a month he still had no job. That he always had money was of deep concern. And then he disappeared for a week. After a few days of being unable to reach him, I desperately began trying to contact high school acquaintances now at colleges in other states. After a couple of days, we learned that he was hanging around his former college—no doubt plying his illegal trade. Larry and I realized we were foolishly enabling this behavior by continuing to pay his rent. We discussed Ashby's situation at night. I investigated residential rehab programs by day. Fortunately, although Larry and I did not always agree, we usually pulled together after wrestling with decisions concerning both boys. One night Larry took Ashby to dinner and offered him a choice: "A drug-rehab program out of town—or—a homeless shelter downtown. Bottom line: we're moving you out of the apartment. It's right or left at Oak Street." Ashby chose to go to the drug-rehab program.

Larry looked at a broad range of possibilities and found a residential therapeutic transition and relapse prevention program in Bend, Oregon that catered to recovering addicts and those with other behavior problems. Its approach consisted of four parts: mindfulness, interpersonal effectiveness, emotional regulation, and distress tolerance. In this year-long, residential program, Ashby would learn life skills like cooking and managing time and money and participate in individual and group therapy and 12-Step meetings. As he progressed, he could transition to the next level where he would be allowed to get a job and attend community college. Larry took Ashby to be interviewed, but Ashby confessed to the head of the program that he was using drugs. As a result, Ashby's acceptance into the program was contingent upon completing a wilderness program and giving up drugs. Theoretically, after the wilderness program, Ashby would go to Bend, where he would work on how to assume responsibility for himself. The plan looked great on paper. The good news, if one can call it that, was that Ashby agreed to go to both programs. We proceeded with cautious optimism.

Based on a recommendation from a friend, we found a wilderness program in Utah that claimed that nine weeks in the wilderness gave troubled young adults time to reflect on their previous actions and the motivation to stop their addiction and to change their behavior. I was not convinced, but we really had no other alternative.

The day before he was to leave for the wilderness program, Ashby vegetated on the sofa as usual but finally managed to throw some clothes in a bag while I loaded the dishwasher. Hearing him approach the kitchen, I said, "Remember the appointment for your physical this afternoon. You have to get one for the wilderness program."

Suddenly, I heard, *"Uhhh!" bam* and the front door slamming shut. I dashed out of the kitchen to find sheet rock particles on the floor. Through the window, I could see Ashby sprinting toward the woods. Next my eyes landed on a jagged, fist-sized hole in the living room wall. I ran outside and into the woods nearby. *"Ashby!—Ashby!—Ash-by! Please answer!"* I got in my car and drove around the neighborhood. I called. I called again and again. Giving up, I returned home to find him hiding in the boys' old fort not far from the house.

After much coaxing, he slouched toward the house with his head down and muttered in a heartrending tone as he swatted small branches aside, *"But I don't want to leave Sugar and the cats!"* Sugar was our twelve-year old black Labrador retriever. "I don't want to be away for a whole year! They might *die* before I come back!"

Despite his difficult behavior in recent years, he always loved and cared for our animals. They responded to the gentle, loving part of him, now hidden inside his outer self that was in conflict with the world. Every night for years he had taken Bully, our fifteen-year old gray calico, to bed with him.

After the hole-in-the-wall incident and the doctor's appointment, Ashby, now utterly spent, lay supine on his bed with Bully purring loudly on his chest. "Bully's your best friend, isn't he?" I whispered.

"Yeah, but I hope he won't always be."

In the wee hours of the next morning in the spring of 2001, Larry, Hunter, and I with puffy eyes were allowed, since the day pre-dated 9/11 and security checks, to walk Ashby somberly through the airport to his gate and hug him good-by. Interestingly, even though Ashby was reluctant, he did not refuse to go. From some motherly intuition, I was confident that he would complete the journey to Utah, but I was still very uncertain about the longer journey.

Traveling alone even with a change of planes in Denver, he arrived at Cortez, Colorado, his destination. He was met by a counselor from the wilderness program and driven to Monticello, Utah. The very fact that he voluntarily changed planes in Denver and arrived at his destination gave us hope. Over the next few weeks we received occasional calls from his drug counselor, far fewer than the literature had promised. "Ashby's — doing — gooood," said his usual cryptic, monotone messages left on the answering machine. One day when I happened to be home and actually talked to the counselor, he said he had finally told Ashby to stop crying. He had cried enough.

I knew Ashby needed to cry. He seldom did, and I knew from my own life that, when telling your story elicits tears, you are in touch with your deepest and most profound truths. It is only then that you can start to release your pent-up angst and begin to heal. Ashby definitely needed to cry. But I did wonder if this was just another one of Ashby's manipulative approaches to get by and pretend to be making progress. The stated purpose of the wilderness program was to try to provide "the appropriate experience, environment, and knowledge so that a person can develop love for himself, his family, and discover the truth of giving and the recognition of belonging." Supposedly, by living in survival mode in the wilderness, hiking with a heavy backpack, cooking one's own food, working as a team, having group therapy, and spending several days alone, one can peel away his outer layers, arrive at his inner core, and start rebuilding.

I was so hoping the program would change Ashby, but I also realized that it was a tall order for only eight weeks. It dangled hope in front of families in crisis when they didn't know where else to turn during these desperate, vulnerable times in their lives. At least for the moment, we were still clinging to optimism with a few loosely stitched threads.

We were not allowed to talk to Ashby during his time there. At home, we were encouraged to attend 12-Step Nar-Anon meetings for families and loved-ones of addicts. We were advised to give up all substances ourselves. One night, almost like a sacred ritual, we purged our house of everything alcoholic—wine, Scotch, Marsala, everything. Over the next several weeks, Larry and I, as part of the required program, wrote letters to Ashby and faxed them to the field office of the wilderness program. They were delivered to Ashby during his forty-eight and seventy-two hour solos in the wilderness. Undistracted, he would have the time and opportunity to focus on his life and experience the support of his family.

In letter number one we were instructed to discuss behaviors that led him to the wilderness program in the first place: our concerns, our fears, what we hoped he would gain from the program.

I wrote mine shortly after he left.

Dear Ashby,

Last night on my way to Kroger, I looked up at the moon, full and white as if it had been pasted against the black sky. I thought about you in the wilderness under the same moon. I remembered other night skies we have viewed together: at the Gulf house where far from city lights we often saw the moon and the Milky Way so clearly and the night on our rafting trip on the San Juan River when you were six, not far from where you are right now, lying on the ground next to our boatman. You connected the North Star with a star in the Big Dipper and identified it as a new constellation -'Ashby's Lance'. We've spoken joyfully of that night since then; we've pointed to your constellation. All of these are vivid, happy memories for me.

However, looking at the moon last night I envisioned you lying there under circumstances far from happy. I thought painfully of how we got from there to here. I remembered you as a little fellow: you wouldn't allow anyone to feed you after ten months; you refused to wear Pampers after your second birthday, strong but positive actions moving toward independence.

In first grade, you had to go down the hall to the reading

tutor. In second grade…a lot of anxiety…third grade…developed a strong resistance to situations and people you disliked…eighth grade, you smoked pot…I hated those meetings with the principal…I worry when I hear you cough. I'm concerned about the harm you're doing to your lungs, your brain, your whole body.

I grew to feel uncomfortable in my own house. I felt like a guard dog, sniffing you every time you passed. That vile, pungent odor hung like a "D" emblazoned on your chest, just like the "A" on Hester Prynne's. In spite of it all, I love you and believe in the sensitive, talented, loving part of you that I know is still there. This is a great opportunity to reflect on your life, and I want to do everything I can to help.

Surely you know I have always loved you; I love you now as much as always and will forever.

Mom

A letter Larry sent him included excerpts from a poem entitled "The Invitation" by Oriah Mountain Dreamer. As Larry said, it presented his longing for a renewed relationship with Ashby.

I want to know what you ache for…
If you dare to dream of meeting your heart's longing…
"Yes!"… If you can sit with pain…if you can be with joy;
I want to know if you can live with failure; yours and mine
And still stand on the edge of the lake
And shout to the silver of the moon,
"Yes!"…

Six weeks after Ashby had entered the program and three

days before Larry, Hunter, and I were scheduled to fly to Utah for the family session at the end of the program, his drug counselor called. "Ma'am, we kicked Ashby out of the program. He did somethin' terrible to another guy's food."

I knew immediately it must have been an irritating person he could not shrug off like the boy he found so annoying in his third-grade class. The counselor continued, "We just' can't trust 'im." With the phone at my ear and my heart racing, I managed to ask, "What—do we do *now*?"

"Well," he offered, "we can send 'im back to you."

"But we sent him to *you*! *You're* the experts!" I cried desperately.

"Well, sometimes we take 'em to Cortez and drop 'em off 'hind Walmart in the weeds and sagebrush. There, nobody'll bother 'im much."

"And then what?" I asked, totally disbelieving this conversation.

"We never lost any of 'em. A couple done went to jail, but eventually they got out. Came back to us or moved on."

Frantically, I dialed Larry. "Listen to this!"

"This really is unbelievable!" he said, "But if this is the expert's advice—the old tough-love approach—guess we should try it."

"You think so?—It scares me to death—But *we* don't know what to do with him. We need to make a decision. You *sure*?—All right—if you really think so. I'll call him back." It was the most difficult call since tough love and consequences had done little to help in the past.

So, the counselor drove Ashby—unbathed for six weeks—an hour east to Cortez, Colorado with his backpack, sleeping bag, and $30 in his camouflage pants. First, he showed Ashby where to find the AA meeting, the labor pool, and the hospital in case "he got in a knife fight." Then he dropped him off behind the super store.

Our son, who had slept under down coverlets and attended private schools all his life, was now homeless.

That first night I felt like a vice was gripping my every muscle, my head, my heart, my entire body. It seemed as if I had a large grapefruit stuck in my throat. *Globus hystericus*, I have since learned it is called. Unable to sleep, I got entangled in the sheets as I tossed through the night. Early next morning a friend from my women's group came by.

"Shannon, *please* reconsider!" she begged. "He's your *child*!"

"I know! But we're at the end of our rope!" I replied emphatically. Larry and I had been indoctrinated with the notion of tough-love in weekly Nar-Anon meetings.

"But still—he's your *child*!" The look of horror on her face no doubt mirrored mine, but it did not change my mind.

The next afternoon the phone rang. It was Ashby calling to say he'd gotten a job in a barbecue restaurant. He would live with the owners and sleep underneath their Fifth Wheel, an expandable trailer with pop-out rooms, in the sleeping bag he had from the wilderness program. Occasional victories like this were enough to keep me clinging to hope that this phase, too, would pass and *some* day he might get his life together.

Two and a half months into his stay in Cortez, the day after his twentieth birthday, Larry and I flew out to see him. We had talked to him; he knew we were coming. The first night, he met us at a Mexican restaurant for dinner where we exchanged awkward hugs. As we ordered dinner, Larry tried to engage him in conversation. "Doing okay?" he asked.

"Yep — fine," Ashby responded matter-of-factly, diverting his eyes from both of us.

"Job going all right?" Larry asked.

"Well, I'm not working at the barbeque restaurant anymore. I'm at a new place. We call it the 'grease pit'. A hamburger place. Can't stay long 'cause I gotta work tonight."

"Oh, okay," I responded in a chipper voice, trying to disguise my disappointment.

We continued our tentative dance of words until we relaxed into a rhythm of conversation of sorts. No, it was really more of a monologue as Ashby told his story:

"…so I quit my job at the barbeque place. John did cocaine. He'd go off sometimes — for two or three days. One night when he was home — at the Fifth Wheel, I mean — he and Susan were drunk. He slapped her around and called her a bitch. She finally stumbled into the kitchen. I heard her rummaging through drawers. Then she went outside and slammed the door.

"I heard her crying that she was gonna kill herself. *I'm gonna kill myself! I'm gonna kill myself*" — I pulled the sleeping bag over my head. But I could still hear her, and she said it again, louder."

"About this time, the kitchen door slammed again. I started hearing a scratching sound. I finally peeked out and saw John dragging Susan by her hair around in the gravel. When he dropped her, he picked up a bag — looked like the money bag from the restaurant — got in his truck and scratched off. I mean, he was outta there."

"I go out of my sleeping bag to see if I could help, I guess to try to be nice. Right then she picked up a big knife. Again, she said she was gonna kill herself! She said John took her for everything she got! She called him a sorry bastard and kept going on and on about killing herself."

"Boy she was freaking me out about now! And I said, 'No, you're not 'cause if you were, you'd've already done it by now. Now gimme that knife!' And she handed it over just like that.

"Man, I didn't like living there."

"I guess not," Larry interjected.

"So I quit my job and moved out."

"And where are you living now?" I asked.

"Oh, with some friends. One of 'em has a Section 8 apartment."

During a pause that hung like morning fog while I was trying to envision his new place, and my eyes shifted from Ashby's oily, disheveled hair and unshaven face to his long, slender fingers—now grimy from the dust and the underbelly of Cortez—as he pushed a tortilla chip around in the salsa.

I interrupted the silence and changed the subject. "Whoa! You have fingernails! How can that be?"

"Well," Ashby said slowly, as he opened his hand to show all five fingers. "Here in Cortez I don't have to live up to *anybody's* expectations—*not anybody's*. I like it here."

I was silent, but my mind raced in disbelief, "He couldn't possibly be in his right mind to *like it here*." I had heard the term *trailer trash* many times. Here and now my own son was living the sordid life I had unabashedly scorned in the past.

We finished dinner rather hurriedly. Waiting for the bill, I stared numbly at Larry, and both of us just shook our heads.

"That's our boy," Larry said mockingly, folding his napkin, shaking his head and calculating the tip as Ashby left to go to work.

The next day, while Ashby was working, Larry and I stopped by the barbeque restaurant and happened to find John, the owner. We learned a lot more about Ashby and his situation in Cortez. John joined us at the table, telling us he had been amazed when Ashby came in and filled out the job application. He noted that Ashby had no home address. John was impressed that Ashby wrote neatly and spelled everything correctly, unlike most of the other applicants who lacked the wherewithal to leave this dusty little town for a higher calling. Larry later told me he was proud that Ashby stood out in this way. We were always grasping for a kernel of hope.

But at the end of our conversation with John, we learned that Ashby was not working anywhere at the moment. The story about the grease pit was a lie. It was not until months later that Ashby admitted that he never had a legitimate job after the barbeque restaurant; he never worked at the "grease pit." Instead he hung out at the apartment with a flock of others on the same road to nowhere. He stole food for survival. He used his fake ID to buy beer for under-age drinkers and charged them a few dollars more than he paid for it. He shop-lifted cigarettes on his way out of the liquor stores, until the day he got caught, was hand-cuffed, and taken to jail. He and a habitual inmate played a game of find-and-seek with a toothpaste cap hidden inside one of the pink slippers they'd been issued. His cell mate's advice was, "Make sure you always got a tooth paste cap." Along with their shoes, the warden had also confiscated their belts. Ashby reported he always had to hold up his sagging jeans so they wouldn't fall off his shrinking waist.

Based on these stories, Larry and I convinced Ashby that he

was travelling a dead-end street and urged him to try to get re-instated in the wilderness program. We asked if his way of life is what he preferred. After some contemplation, Ashby decided it might be better to finish the wilderness program and move on to Bend. So, Ashby called the program office and, as we listened to Ashby's end of the phone conversation, he masterfully lied to the counselor that he had attended AA meetings faithfully and had had a major change in attitude. His glib words were a reminder of his ability to manipulate others and the reasons we had lost our trust in him … or more truthfully had lost our son altogether. The next morning, the counselor drove sixty miles east to Cortez and picked him up. Ashby returned to the wilderness program. Three weeks later we got a call that we should plan to attend the family session that marked the conclusion of the program.

Larry, Hunter, and I flew to Utah and spent one of the most intense times our family has ever experienced together. For three days, we sat face-to-face and one by one spilled our truths to each other, the good and the painful.

Ashby complained that Larry was never home and that I was too nosey. The family meeting included three other fami-lies and was facilitated by a wise, extraordinary woman with gray hair and dark, weathered skin; she was able to extract truth from the most reluctant person. We realized that Ashby wanted to be independent but could not be responsible for himself and so re-sented everything we did. The most significant moment—the game-changer—was that Hunter cried (for one of the first times ever) and talked about how Ashby had abandoned his animals and about how Ashby had hurt Hunter and himself. As usual, Ashby convinced everyone that he had changed his behavior.

He apologized for what he had done to Hunter, but he was less forthcoming with Larry and me.

Completing the wilderness program allowed Ashby to then go to the program in Bend. I was the designated parent to take him there. Larry and Hunter flew home to Atlanta, and Ashby and I headed to Bend where, at last, he would enroll in the year-long life-skills program.

Six weeks into the program in Bend came another dreaded call, in August of 2001. With Ashby and the director of the program on speaker phone, we learned that Ashby had stood up and admitted in a group session that he had smoked pot and drunk alcohol since he'd been in the program and that he had told fellow participants he could help them get illegal substances. He was told to pack his things immediately and be out of there before nightfall.

During our initial conversation, Larry told Ashby to call us from a pay phone as soon as he moved out. He wanted the two of us to have time to discuss our own reactions and plans to Ashby's latest bump in the road. Having gone through this drill before, we were not as shell-shocked as the time before. After some discussion, we agreed that Ashby should go and make his way on the streets in Bend.

After the shock of dealing with another Ashby failure, we refocused on the fact that we had paid a non-refundable $50,000 to the program up front. Larry was panicked and called the director to "discuss" the matter. The initial response was it was the policy to not refund any of the money. Larry kept pressing, and we finally got reimbursed, but the amount was far short of the prorated share that we should have gotten. We later learned that many of these programs take financial advantage of desperate families who pressure their children to enter these programs. Because many children do not want to change their behavior and only enter these programs reluctantly, they often fail to complete them. At the same time, parents are still responsible for the full costs of the program.

In October of 2001, shortly after 9/11, Ashby had now been on the streets of Bend for close to two months. From occasional phone calls, we knew that so far he had lived in three different apartments with various "graduates" of the program who were usually working. Inevitably, each group of roommates had summarily kicked him out. He had no money and was making no effort to get a job. One day a young woman called to say that her group had kicked him out because he was stealing their food. Ashby was again living on the streets. The young woman also reported that Ashby had not taken his backpack or sleeping bag when they put him out. She wanted to know what they should do with his stuff.

We were concerned since it was now late October, and temperatures in Bend were dipping below freezing. The Wednesday night after this phone conversation with Ashby's last group of roommates, Larry turned to me without mincing words. "Are you going to Bend tomorrow to find Ashby, or am I?"

There was little discussion. Larry had just had a minor heart surgery procedure and could not travel. It was up to me to go but I didn't mind. I still had some hope that we could make a difference; I felt it was my duty. At noon the next day, I boarded a plane and flew to Bend, Oregon.

During the five-hour flight that seemed to last a lifetime, I fretted over where I would begin my search. I jiggled my leg for a while. Would I find him? I chewed on my pen. Would he be beaten up and left under a bush for dead? I tried to read. Would he have overdosed? Where would I take him if I found him? Based on the recommendation of a staff member in the Bend program, who suspected that Ashby had a personality disorder, we had investigated a mental health treatment center north of New York City. It seemed like another possibility, but I wondered if he would even consider going to another program. Finally, exhausted from all these ruminations, I pushed my seat back and escaped into sleep.

As I drove the rental car into Bend with the afternoon sun low in the autumn sky, my eyes watered from the blinding orb. I got lost, turned around, and found my way to the hotel; I rolled my luggage into the room and looked at my watch. It was 7 PM. It was Thursday, and I wasn't scheduled to leave until Sunday. What would I do with Ashby for three days if I found him right away?

I called the apartment where he had last lived and asked if I could pick up his belongings. I then had a chance to meet these young people who were so-called graduates of the program that Ashby had briefly attended. They were now working and it *appeared* they were leading fairly productive lives, although much later Ashby informed me that most of them were not, a comment that made me wonder if any of these programs were truly beneficial to their participants and worthy of the exorbitant fees they charged. After chatting briefly with his most recent roommates, I asked where I should begin my search. Offering to help me after lunch the next day, one fellow suggested we start in the city park where the "park rats," the name for the local street kids, hung out.

On my way back, I drove a few blocks past the hotel to the park to determine whether I should drive or walk there the next day. Night was falling on the charming, laid-back town of Bend, its center lined with attractive one- and two-story shops and eateries with parking on the street. I drove the entire length of the beautiful park where the Deschutes River gracefully meanders. At one end of the park I had noticed people milling around in a parking lot, and, as I turned the car around to start back to the hotel—on a sheer whim—I turned into it. As I approached the end of the lot, I saw, standing in a circle, several young men on a level ten feet above me. They appeared to be playing hackie-sack, bouncing a small bean-filled bag off a foot, a knee, a shoulder or other body part, to another person in the circle. In the dim light, I noticed a tall, thin, fair-skinned man with a shaved head.

"Is that Ashby? Could it possibly be?"

I pulled into a parking space, leaned out on my left leg and said tentatively, almost in a whisper, "Ash-by?" The bald-headed person suddenly jerked his head from side to side as if hearing strange voices.

"Ash-by?" I uttered a little louder—and then with everything I had, "ASH-BY!"

Finally spotting me, he shouted, "MOM!"

On my flight west, the thought had occurred to me that he might run away when he saw me, but instead, he raced toward me with open arms. "Mom, is that really *you*?" He touched my arm again to make sure. "*How* did you get here? — *Why* are you here?"

"I flew out today. I'm here because *I love you.*" I paused. I wanted to cry for joy but instead gathered my wits as I glanced at my watch. I had found him in an hour and a half after arriving in a town of 52,000.

"Had dinner?" I knew the answer before I asked. Within five minutes we were ordering Mexican food in a nearby restaurant.

"Mom, I want to say two things: first, I'm going to stay in Bend; second, I'm going to keep smoking pot."

"You're legally old enough to make your own life choices, but you don't have to make up your mind this minute. Today's Thursday; I'll be here till Sunday morning. Pop and I are offering you one more opportunity, a treatment center in New York. But tomorrow I want to ship your coverlet, pillows, bike and a few other things back to Atlanta. No use in throwing them away."

"Oh, no." He dropped his head. "I pawned my bike yesterday."

"How much did you get for it?"

"Eighty dollars," he said sheepishly, his head still down.

"And we paid over four hundred dollars just a few weeks ago? First thing tomorrow we're buying it back and shipping it to Atlanta."

"One more thing, Mom." He stuck out his tongue. At the sight of his tongue ring, I turned my head and almost regurgitated my guacamole salad.

"Okay," I said, regaining my composure. "I don't want to see it again."

In spite of the circumstances, we had a pleasant dinner. He was truly glad to see me, and I, having just returned from a wonderful, rejuvenating trip to Japan, felt calm, filled-up, patient, and resilient. I was exceedingly happy that I had found him in such good physical health. He reminded me a couple of times that he was going to stay in Bend and smoke pot. And I reminded him not to rush his decision. I again mentioned the treatment program in New York.

"I don't want any more programs. I'm sick of 'em."

After dinner, waiting for our check, I offered him a shower at my hotel.

"Sure; that'd be good," he replied, "but I'm not going to spend the night."

After a long, steamy shower, he put his dirty clothes back on.

"Want to watch TV?" I asked.

"Yeah, sure." He immediately sank into the other bed and nestled in among the pillows. After twenty minutes, he appeared to have completely relaxed. He sighed. "Well…I just might spend the night after all." Within minutes he was asleep.

The next morning, we found the pawn shop, bought his bike back for more than he had gotten for it the day before and shipped it to Atlanta. We went to a house where he had lived for a week and collected boxes of dirty clothes from the basement. As we went about these tasks, I was struck yet again that for some time Ashby had been following a path of unseemly patterns of shapes, textures, and innuendos. They were completely foreign to me. I could not identify with any aspects of his life.

In the hotel laundry room, we washed his clothes. We folded and folded some more. Later, as we sorted and packed, I held up his hiking boots. "Want to keep these or ship them to Atlanta?"

"They'll be kinda heavy, carrying them around Bend and all."

"Yeah," I responded, "but it's going to start snowing pretty soon. You might need them. And, if you decide to go to New York, it snows there, too."

"Oh, yeah—forgot about that. Don't ship 'em back." Then holding up two bags, he asked, "Mom, should I keep the duffel or just the backpack?"

I managed to keep a straight face. "Ashby, sorry, but I have no experience on the streets. That'll have to be your decision."

Occasionally during my three-day stay, I stole away to the parking lot for cell phone reception. I called Larry, a sibling, or a friend to keep them posted but mostly to keep myself grounded.

A little earlier in the laundry room, Ashby had piped up, "Mom, I kinda—sorta—wanna…" I kept folding clothes and didn't look his way. I had a hunch of what he was trying to say. An hour later, after trying to decide which bag to keep in Bend, he said, "Mom, I think I want a better life."

"Yeah?" I responded nonchalantly, not even looking his way.

"I think—I wanna go to New York," he said.

"Why is that? I thought you liked it here."

"Well, it's not really *that* great—on the streets, I mean. I think I want a better life."

"Oh, that's interesting," I said, continuing to pack, blasé on the outside, my heart racing on the inside.

"But since I'm going to be leaving, I want to go out tonight and tell everyone good-by."

Before he went out, we went to a Chinese restaurant for dinner. After we finished I cracked open my fortune cookie: "Patience is the best remedy for every trouble." And Ashby tore into his: "Believe in yourself." Almost in synch we slipped them into our wallets.

I dropped him off where he requested, and he agreed to be back at the hotel early the next morning. I went to bed not knowing if he would reappear on time, or at all. I slept well, nonetheless, and at 5:58 AM I heard a knock at the door. Recognizing Ashby through the peephole, I opened it. He presented me with a perfect white rose he had picked in a public park. I gave him a hug.

I nursed the rose all the way to New York and later home to Atlanta where it remained in a small vase for several years until it fell apart.

We left the hotel and headed for the airport, spending the entire day en route to LaGuardia. After landing in New York, we spent the night at a nearby hotel. The next morning, we were picked up by a limousine sent by the treatment center to take us on our trip north. Ashby, thin as a rail, wore his usual sagging pants, loop earrings, tongue ring, silver chain around his neck, and skinned head. I dressed for whatever might unfold for, by now, I never knew what might happen. The view, as we rode up the Anne Hutchinson River Parkway, was lovely. We wound our way northward on the divided highway beneath occasional arched, stone bridges toward the unknown. Our well-dressed driver, a college student from Brazil, chatted the entire way. His banter, like a mental deflector that switches into place at the most opportune times, temporarily steered my thoughts away from our reality.

After arriving at the mental health treatment center in Brewster, New York, each of us met individually with the two directors. Afterwards, Ashby was escorted to his entry-level living quarters with the tightest confinement, a carriage-house-turned dorm with video surveillance. He was stripped of his own clothing and jewelry and issued basic sweat pants and tee shirts.

I left the next day without seeing Ashby again. We were committed to having him survive this world so we invested $19,000 a month, and we hoped that this time we had found a program that would work. After returning to Atlanta, I told Larry the story of the entire journey even though he had already heard much of it. Larry was astonished at all I had gone through and was appreciative of what I had accomplished. We waited anxiously for Ashby to call.

The intake counselor had described strict limitations of the first part of their program, and we knew that Ashby would not be thrilled. In effect, he was being incarcerated, and that was an anathema to him. When he did call, he exclaimed in a high-pitched voice, "*The people here are crazy.* I mean really *crazy!*" He angrily demanded to know how we could possibly have done this to him. But we breathed more calmly and slept more soundly knowing he was safe and had food and shelter and was under tight supervision of staff members highly trained to help addicts.

After three weeks, he transitioned to level two called PAT (pre-apartment training). It was not as tightly monitored and was located in a three-story, blue Victorian house atop a hill on a generous parcel of land with towering, leafless hardwoods. The first day he was there Ashby began his daily regimen of meetings with various groups—drug rehab, personality disorder, individual therapy, art therapy, and others. His counselors admitted that they knew nothing about DM and told Ashby to go on-line, educate himself, and teach the professional staff about it. At the same time, he reported to us that he was gaining weight, welcome news after his two stints on the streets.

His counselors at the program were all trained to deal with drug addiction. The leader had come up with a sniff test, a novel approach to find out where a participant was in his recovery. The counselors would check a person's pulse, then have him smell the pot that was in a box. If the pulse rate increased, he failed the test and would take a follow up test each week until his pulse remained steady. I never asked, but I suspect that Ashby's pulse had never slowed down during the program and probably had not since his first encounter with marijuana in the seventh grade. I was afraid his addiction was a permanent condition, but I refused to give up.

After another month, Ashby was allowed to move to the third level of the program, called SDL (self-directed living). This time he lived in an apartment with two roommates; he had less structure and was allowed to work. He decided to volunteer for the Muscular Dystrophy Association. His transportation was expensive and was over and above what we were already paying for the program. After a few weeks, we told him he had to find a paying job. Home Depot hired him at $10 an hour in the paint department where he worked as many hours as possible in order to stay away from the treatment center.

But, after living in his apartment for about four months, he was caught drinking again. As Larry said, we could not call it a "relapse" because Ashby probably had never committed to being sober in the first place, and when the opportunity presented itself, Ashby started drinking again. At first, Ashby had bought a bottle of vodka and hid it down the street in a cemetery. He and another person from the program began an evening ritual of taking a "walk" to the cemetery. They were able to hide their drinking from the staff for at least a while. Then one night he and his friend got permission to take two girls on a date to the movies. While out, they bought another bottle of vodka and drank it all. Of course, when they returned to the apartment, they were obviously drunk. As a result, the directors of the center made Ashby quit his job and move back to the tightest level of confinement. He was again stripped of his own clothing and jewelry and issued basic sweat pants and tee shirts. There he lived for the next four months. Yet again, we were disappointed, but by this time we also were numb.

Soon after on Memorial Day 2002, Larry, always at his computer before daybreak, shared with Ashby a Vietnam experience from his time in the Navy. As he wrote, Bully, Ashby's favorite cat of all time, rested peacefully in his lap on one of his final days. Sadly, Bully had recently been diagnosed with cancer.

Ashby,

I don't know if I have ever shared this story with you. It's always sad for me to recount, but I relive it every Memorial Day.

I graduated from Georgia Tech in 1965, and the Vietnam War was at its most intense period. At that time everyone was drafted, so I chose the Navy Seabees because it was the closest thing to architecture. Navy Seabees means I did construction work in a Construction Battalion (CB, or Seabee.)

I was in Vietnam twice. Didn't know I was such a fool until later. On my first tour, I was an assistant company commander, responsible for 130 Seabees doing work for the Marines throughout the northern part of South Vietnam.

My story begins with an assignment from Da Nang to a place north of Chu Lai. I was taking a group of Seabees to survey and layout an airfield that was to be used for a surprise landing. We arrived at daybreak and began our work. We could hear firefights in the distance…closer than I had been to them before. But we had work to do and soon we were not distracted. In early afternoon before our work was finished, a Marine came to me and told me we needed to leave. He said the Vietcong were getting too close and we would have to return after the area was secured. We called in the helicopter to take us back to our base. Soon after lift-off, I took off my flak jacket and was relieved to survey the dense jungle from a safe distance. A few minutes after we departed, the helicopter turned back inland and the machine gunner sitting next to me motioned me to put my flak jacket back on. I leaned over and asked what was happening. He said we were going to pick up some wounded Marines.

As we flew over treetops, I finally saw an open area about the size of a baseball diamond. The pilot began his descent into the opening, which barely had room for the blades to miss the trees. As we descended, I saw white flashes, which momentarily I paid no attention to until the machine gunner next to me started firing. I then recognized that the white flashes were people shooting at us. In the next few minutes as we landed, picked up the wounded Marines and lifted off again, I cannot remember much, but I went through four magazines with my M-14. Eighty rounds and a hot barrel with a machine gun in my left ear are about all the details I remember. But from then on, the details were too vivid.

We lifted off safely and I turned my attention to the wounded

Marines. A young man which I would say was 17 or 18 was right by me. I tried to see what I could do. He was crying loudly and asking for help. So much of his side was exposed and bleeding. I nearly threw up. I yelled for someone to help but all the Marines were hurt badly and needed help. We had no corpsman on the helicopter. I tried to find something to try to stop the bleeding but realized that all I could do was hold him. I was told we were headed to a hospital ship not too far off shore. As he lay there in my arms, he finally lost consciousness. I tried to do something to save him but it was futile. All I could do was hold him tight. We finally arrived at the hospital ship and the corpsmen on the ship took him off the helicopter. I asked if they thought he was going to survive. I could tell by the way they looked at him that the answer was no. I cried then and I cry whenever I tell the story. Then as now, I could not understand where God was in all of this. I still don't understand.

This day always makes me think of the young Marine... younger than you. Now it makes me think of you. But you are alive and have a chance to live a life that matters. I will remember that Marine forever. I will have hopes for you each day of your life.

Thanks for reading this.

Pop

A few days later, Ashby called. "Pop," he said, "that was an incredible story...I feel like I've been in a war all my life, and I'm that wounded soldier...and I like knowing you're holding me tight. I'm carrying Bully and your story in my back pocket," a metaphor probably borrowed from one of his therapy groups.

After Ashby returned to the restrictive program, we called to tell him that his favorite living being, his cat Bully, had a large, inoperable tumor and would likely not survive until he returned. In addition to sleeping with Ashby every night when he was younger, Ashby had sometimes dressed Bully in my old doll dresses and slung him around his neck for a stroll through the house. Bully had infinite patience and brought love and levity to our household.

We had promised to let Ashby know if anything happened to the animals. And so it was, a few weeks later, we had to call and relay the devastating news. Bully had died. Hunter volunteered to tell him. There, in his tightly controlled environment, stripped of his identity, Ashby had to wrestle with this loss. He later told us he cried for the first time since being at this treatment center, and he said he cried for days. During that time, he later told us, he started wondering what else he would miss if he continued his life in the same pattern.

After the death of Bully, Larry and I were heading to New York for another meeting with Ashby and his psychologist. We had agreed ahead of time that we would dwell on the positive aspects of Ashby, his talents and the good things he had done in his life, not his problems and what he lacked. During the session, we reminded him about his learning strengths identified in his psychological profile done a year and a half earlier when he entered the program in New York:

"He ... [has] internal fortitude — insight about his learning
profile — desire to perform well — [good] non-verbal reasoning
...visual imagery for the overview (gestalt) and details (non-aca-

demic)... enjoyment and skills in artistic activities (e.g., photography and ceramics)—learning through participation—response to encouragement, support and success—persistence, effort, positive attitude, and interactive style within a one-on-one situation."

We talked about his above average IQ and verbal scores and performance scores that catapulted him to the 95th percentile. We spoke of his visual gifts and how we proudly display his pottery slabs and turned pots, drawings, and photographs throughout our house. We recalled his many successes on the soccer field.

Ashby smiled a lot during the session. Nestled in that tiny room that day, at least for a while, I think he truly believed he was not stupid. But eventually he reached the end of his attention span and started squirming, as he had done all those times when I tried to help him study for exams. At some point, he would inevitably come to a screeching halt, and it was impossible to re-engage him.

Soon after our visit, the director approached Larry to see if one of us would speak at the annual family conference about the benefits of the program and how it had helped our son. I, at that point, was not sure that the program had lived up to what they had promised, but Larry thought that Ashby had learned some important lessons and was making progress. Later, Larry came to believe that the program was a farce and that his testimony about its benefits was more wishful thinking than truth.

During this time, I continued my weekly meetings with my women's group and would always give them the latest update on Ashby. I recall someone saying and others echoing that I must do something for myself. I was continuing to create, painting furniture, writing short stories, and working in my garden. I had also been toying with the idea of building a studio, a place of my own. So, I got in touch with Amy, an architect who worked at Larry's office, to help me design a studio. Amy and I worked through many schemes until we arrived at one that would accomplish what I wanted—a large area for creating art with places for a microwave, toilet, shower, and storage. Once designed, my brother who lived in North Carolina and his son came to build the studio. I was so excited, and I watched the construction with great anticipation, dreaming of how it would be when finished. However, progress was slow, and after the exterior was complete, I had to tell my brother that we could no longer afford him. Larry and I decided we would complete the interior ourselves. As it turned out, this project rekindled the excitement of doing something together, reminding us of our earlier years, before we had children. Each afternoon, Larry would get home around 5:30 which he had not done for years. We would eat dinner and then move to the studio to continue our work. We always made sure to "measure twice in order to cut only once" and celebrated each board that fit properly into place. It was a renewed joy that provided a much needed break from the constant worry about Ashby.

But inevitably those concerns about Ashby's struggles crept back into our lives. That summer we were summoned to yet another meeting with Ashby and his psychologist. During the session, I asked Ashby if he could shed more light on the war he was in and asked who the enemy was.

"Well," he said, "school was always hard—and I always felt stupid—and then the myotonic dystrophy..." Indeed, he was fighting his *own* war on a battlefield spotted with white flashes.

"So, you've been wounded. Do you think there's any possibility for healing?" I asked.

Glancing out the window toward the vegetable garden where a brown rabbit suddenly appeared, he thought for a moment. "Well. I guess I could look at it like this: I'm on a hospital ship, and soon I'll be well enough to leave."

In September of 2002, when Ashby had been in the program for close to a year and had turned twenty-one, Larry and I decided that it was time for him to leave the program. We weren't convinced that he was ready, but in a two-year period we had spent upwards of $200,000 on three different treatment programs. At this point we were not sure he was making progress; and we were not willing to continue depleting our savings. Insurance had covered very little. When we told Ashby that we were taking him out, he decided that, rather than return to Atlanta, he would continue to live in Brewster, NY in order to be close to the treatment center and in touch with his counselors. We wanted to believe that but how could we be so naïve after all we knew?

Before he moved into his new apartment, we allowed Ashby to return home for a two-day visit, his first in a year and a half since he left for the wilderness program. While he was there, we packed pillows, sheets, and clothes, some of which had been shipped to Bend and back a couple of years before. He visited with us and hugged the two remaining animals. Then he and I headed north in Larry's eight-year-old Oldsmobile, a bona fide clunker that hardly fit the cool image Ashby would have liked to portray. Nevertheless, he expressed gratitude for transportation at all. He drove the entire way, 962 miles, stopping only in Staunton, Virginia to sleep for a few hours, then continuing up the Shenandoah Valley. We talked almost non-stop.

On the second day I said, "Ashby, you've made a good choice to live in New York for now—away from the treatment center, but close enough to stay in touch with your counselor. He likes you a lot; he *wants* you to succeed. He believes you can do it; but it's up to you."

I wanted desperately to believe he was making the right choice.

Ashby replied with a hint of his early childhood enthusiasm, "Yeah. It'll be like learning to ride a bike! They'll run along beside me and then one day…"

I could almost feel myself running with my hand on the seat of his two-wheeler in the church parking lot with his golden locks blowing in the wind as he maneuvered the bike in the sloping lot. In those days, self-confidence exuded from his every pore before he hit the impenetrable wall of academics and a brain that failed him. Silence filled the car as I gazed beyond the horizon and tilted my head back slightly to prevent the inevitable tears from escaping down my cheeks. I put on my sun glasses and shifted my weight and paused to gather my composure.

Such a long trip afforded ample time to reflect on our lives, a journey I could never have imagined. A year and a half ago, Ashby had divulged, during the family meeting at the end of the wilderness program, that when he was eleven, after he was diagnosed with DM, he felt different from everyone—*not normal*. He felt stupid and incompetent. He watched his peers soaring ahead of him in school. Bewilderment, inferiority, and fear started eating at his core as he approached adolescence, a time when he wanted to be *just like everyone else*. But like a colony of termites sneaking in unnoticed until major damage is done, the deterioration of his self-esteem had probably begun in kindergarten when he couldn't learn to read, even though he wanted to.

As we drove along, we spoke about a night in high school. We were outside talking. I was standing and he was sitting on the hood of a car. As we reflected on the event after a trip to the principal's office earlier that day for yet another offense, the tone of the conversation went from belligerence to denial to guilt, and finally Ashby said, "I don't know *why* I keep doing all these stupid things."

"What made you change your attitude?" I asked. "Were your counselors [in the New York program] helpful?"

"Well, sort of. But I'm the one who had to do the work," he professed. I recognized a familiar tone: Intellectually, he knew the right thing to say; but his words sounded empty to my experienced ears.

"Was there a turning point?" I asked.

"Yeah. It was Bully. That was the hardest thing."

"Mom," he spoke with a genuine tone of concern. "Did you spend some of the money you inherited from your mom—I mean—on my programs?"

"Yes," I answered, "some of it."

"Oh, I just *hate* that."

I finally dredged up a response. "You know, Ashby, your grandmother always said, 'people are more important than things.'"

Neither of us spoke for several miles as we pushed past eighteen-wheelers on I-81 toward New York. A cloudless, cerulean sky spread like an elusive canopy encapsulating us in a bubble of hope and illusion.

The day was good, extremely good.

In Brewster, New York, Ashby dabbled at independence for several months, working, earning and managing money, handling a checkbook, eating properly, being on time to work, choosing healthy recreational pastimes, getting enough sleep, avoiding anxiety-provoking situations, staying focused, controlling obsessive thinking patterns and impulsivity, and perhaps his biggest challenge — trying to stay sober in order to accomplish all of these. At least, these were his goals, and Larry and I hoped he was working toward them. But we sensed early on that they were not really part of his agenda, and we knew from the past that he was often dishonest and just did not know how to deal with independence.

As information slipped out during our phone calls about his renewed independence, we began to suspect that he was on another slippery slope. Six months later, the bubble of illusion that had encapsulated us on our trip north burst, as bubbles are wont to do. Ashby resumed drinking and smoking pot; he was fired from two jobs; he didn't eat well; he kept erratic hours; he rear-ended another car; he had to go to court and pay a fine. Again, he found himself rudderless with no control over his money, his life, his anything.

Larry and I equivocated once again over what to do next. We agreed that I would fly to New York and bring him home so that we would at least know he was safe. In January of 2003, after packing Ashby out of his ill-kept rented room and getting on the road in mid-afternoon, we drove 17 hours straight through to Atlanta. Unlike our cozy conversational trip going north six months earlier, we talked very little.

After Ashby's two-year absence that included homelessness and living in the underbelly of life, Larry and I tried to re-domesticate him in areas like bathing regularly, brushing his teeth, washing his clothes, and using good manners, vestiges of our own up-bringing that we had tried to instill in him as a child.

In the past eleven years that Ashby has been living in our home again, he has held and lost several jobs. For nearly a year, he managed to keep a part-time administrative position in the office of a competitive soccer club where he played for many years while in school. He opened a checking account and assumed paying his phone bill. But mostly he has been unemployed. He sometimes gets jobs but quickly loses them because he does not show up or is frequently tardy. He has totaled three cars. He has experimented with several new drugs that he learned about in the treatment centers. According to him, after hearing such amazing things about them, *he just had to try them*. He has sold drugs. He has gotten two DUIs and has lost his license for a year each time. He has been to jail three times. He has tried unsuccessfully to live with roommates and each time has had to move back home.

We struggled with how to provide support for Ashby without having to live with his drug use and unkempt life style. Reluctantly, we made the decision for me to give up my beloved studio, three years after it had been completed. We let Ashby live there because it is near to the house but separate, and he would not have to pay rent. He spends his days watching television and playing videogames.

In terms of social life, Ashby sees his old friend Adam who has been a constant support since seventh grade. But most of his other "friends" are connected to his drug selling and use. He is reluctant to spend much time with the family. Even though he has little money, he always prefers to eat out by himself or with his friends.

As life speeds past, I've noted that each time his external structure is removed, Ashby loses his North Star. The psychologist at the treatment center in New York once commented that it is as if Ashby were missing his central core. He has difficulty maintaining consistency and motivation for anything for very long: school, abstinence, household chores, and a job. At successful moments, we try to acknowledge and celebrate every small positive step. But Larry and I are wise enough not to get overly excited because, when we have in the past, Ashby has always shot himself in the foot. These days, hope seems ever more elusive.

Reflecting back on Ashby's turbulent adolescence and young adulthood, I have wondered what role DM—its actual symptoms and the fact of knowing about it—has played in both the physical and emotional realms. Sometimes not knowing the truth is excruciatingly difficult for parents who sense intuitively that something is wrong with their child but cannot get a definitive diagnosis. At the same time, knowing the truth is also challenging. Genetic testing has been a boon to research and treatment for many diseases, but it presents many ethical and practical dilemmas. Who should be tested and at what age? If a child learns the truth very early, what psychological devastation may he face? Yet what are the costs of withholding that information? As Ashby eloquently said in his late twenties, "I wish I hadn't known about myotonic dystrophy when I was eleven. Well, no, wait! If you had known and kept it a secret, boy, I'd be really mad."

With hindsight, I began to sense that every time we introduced a new kind of support or treatment, Ashby was reminded that he was not okay. Interventions that had worked for Hunter seemed to backfire with Ashby. I came to understand what Jean Piaget, the Swiss philosopher and psychologist, espoused in the mid-twentieth century: *if you treat children the same, you treat them unjustly*. I also frequently reminded myself that *unmet expectations are the root of all conflict* and try to see Ashby for who he is and not who I want him to be.

Within the nature-nurture controversy it's hard to tease out the root causes of behavior, but I firmly believed that beneath Ashby's defiance, anger, anxiety, inattention, and impulsivity, lay a sad, fearful young man who felt utterly powerless over what was happening inside his brain and to his body. He was keenly aware of himself in the world and acutely perceptive of how he failed to measure up to his peers, unlike Hunter who was aloof and oblivious to much around him.

Ashby's plea was, "I just want to be normal."

Hunter's attitude was, "Whatever…"

In the process of writing this book, I asked Ashby how *he* feels about all of this. After several weeks, he still had not sat down—or was unable to sit down and focus long enough to write something—so I finally made a suggestion: I would ask questions; he would talk; I would serve as scribe. And so we spent three hours over several days creating a time line, starting in kindergarten. After several more weeks and much prodding, he finally wrote the following:

> To me, DM has impacted my life a lot. The progression of this disease is the part that gets to me the most. I feel that I will become a lot worse. The hardest thing for me is seeing my brother

and how he is affected; it makes me think I will get as bad as him one day. I've noticed these things:

- Myotonia in hands (hurts sometime, prevents me from performing certain tasks)
- Myotonia in my tongue makes me talk funny and feel self-conscious.
- DM has held me back physically and this hurts me because I can't progress like those around me. (I can't put on muscle mass.)
- In school, I thought people were progressing beyond where I was. I didn't think I could achieve these levels because of the disease. And what was the point in trying if I couldn't succeed?
- In the past 3 or 4 years, I notice more and more myotonia in tongue and hands.
- The muscles in my neck are sore all the time.

The worst thing is that I can't change this and it has damaged me psychologically. If I was playing poker with the hand I was dealt in life, I would fold. That is how DM makes me feel.

PART III

ACTIVISM

10. Contacting the Hunter Family

Once Ashby and I had been definitively diagnosed as having myotonic dystrophy, I faced an ethical dilemma. For the seven previous years, ever since Hunter's diagnosis, I had been a student of myotonic dystrophy and its myriad symptoms. I was still learning new ways that this gene could affect our lives, like stubbornness, obsessive tendencies, personality disorders, gonadal atrophy, insulin resistance, and on and on. It was hard to believe that one abnormal gene could wreak such havoc. It was now apparent to me that certain relatives believed to have the *Hunter disease* actually had *myotonic dystrophy*. The Hunter branch of my family included about twenty first cousins in my mother's generation, most of whom now had children, grandchildren, and some even great grandchildren. Did anyone else in the family know what the *Hunter disease* really was? Were there family members who knew they had myotonic dystrophy and weren't telling? Surely there were relatives who had it and didn't know. Why had some of them died so young, like my grandmother? And what did muscle disease have to do with school and social challenges anyway? Did tales of wedding rings in sock drawers, dates with John Wayne, and gifts of used lipsticks figure into the story?

These memories prompted me to consider how each of us is part of something bigger than our immediate family, bigger than our day-to-day lives, our own problems and idiosyncrasies. Is there merit in thinking collectively of ourselves as a family that also includes future generations? Would our extended family want to take action to help stop the progression of our disease? If I revealed this information in a letter to relatives or publicly divulged my immediate family story, would I cause them untold and possibly unnecessary fear, anger, and embarrassment? Would I violate their privacy by intruding on their denial and desire to let nature take its course—"let go and let God"? Did they hold tight to the maxim that *silence is a virtue*? If I did not tell the story to those who would appreciate knowing it, would I do them an injustice? Quite agitated about my ethical responsibility to my family, I ruminated on these questions often. At the time, I didn't understand the role of a geneticist and had never heard of genetic counseling.

Furthermore, our diagnosis long predated much discussion about the ethical quandaries inherent in genetic research. In fact, in the mid-1990s, when Larry and I offered to sponsor an annual lecture on the ethics of genetics at the School of Public Health at Emory, the dean graciously declined our offer, saying that it was too hot a topic. It was not until the World Health Organization's 2003 publication, "Review on Ethical Issues in Medical Genetics" that the dilemma between the great promise for the advancement of human health and the potential risks to families and individuals with genetic disabilities became widely recognized.

I knew that the material I had gathered would benefit my family members. But how would they react? My Southern upbringing had indoctrinated me with the idea that gentleness, kindness, and consideration for others usually trumped conflict and direct confrontation; in short, I was taught to be *nice*. The possibility existed that some family members would not think kindly of the messenger for delivering unsolicited information of this sort. But I had already begun to shed my "nice" veneer carefully layered on me in childhood. Was I tough enough and willing to handle their responses?

I contacted Mary, companion to my Cousin Helen for nearly thirty years. She was the only other person I knew who had seen the course of this disease up close. She intimated that Helen's father, my great uncle, had a hard time accepting Helen's condition and grew quite impatient when she began having difficulty climbing stairs. Mary had been hired as a *companion* when Helen was in her late twenties and still mobile. She entertained Helen, provided motivation and external structure, even took her on trips to Florida in winter and to baseball games in Atlanta. In essence, *she gave Helen a life*. But, as the disease progressed, Mary also assumed responsibilities as caregiver and nurse. She took heroic measures to clear mucous from Helen's throat with her fingers when declining muscle weakness prevented Helen from coughing it up and caused her to choke.

The dilemma, fueled by my persistent curiosity, gnawed at me, and I could not let it go. Finally, seven years after Hunter's diagnosis, I began composing a letter in my head, and then with pen and paper, writing multiple versions over a period of a month, until one day I started typing; by then, the words spilled onto the page. I was interrupted when my aunt called with news from Mobile. Since my mother had died a few years before, this relative had kept me abreast of family matters.

When she finished talking, I chimed in, "How ironic that you called today. I'm writing to our Hunter branch to tell them what the *Hunter disease* really is. As you well know, Hunter was diagnosed seven or eight years ago—then Ashby and I a few years later."

I suddenly remembered my aunt had difficulty accepting Hunter's diagnosis. When my mother told her, she said, "You've just ruined my day." But I hoped by now she had grown accustomed to it.

I continued, "I wish I had known about this before I had children. If someone had known and hadn't bothered to tell me, I'd be furious. I've learned so much about *myotonic dystrophy*—that's the correct name—these last few years, and most doctors don't know anything about it. I think some of the younger Hunters, especially if they're *thinking* about having children, might want to know."

I paused for a minute and could hear her breathing at the other end. I continued. "I mean, *I* would certainly want to know. It can affect much more than muscles—all kinds of organs like the heart and eyes and the brain—and anesthesia can be risky. I have all the names on Cousin Marian's family tree. What do you think?"

Again pausing, I waited for a response, but she said nothing. I continued talking ever faster to fill the void. "...and amniocentesis can detect whether an unborn child is affected..." I stopped again. "Are you there?"

I waited. Still no response. I rocked nervously in my swivel chair. I waited for what seemed like minutes until she finally spoke. *"Shannon — I have to hang up — I can't take any more — If you decide to mail this letter, I hope you make people want to act, rather than commit suicide."*

Could I or *should* I follow my guts and heart and share this disturbing truth that would obviously disturb many family members?

Now *I* was unable to find words. My mind flashed back to a conversation on her front steps when I was ten; she tried to discourage me from becoming a *writer* because, she said, *so many people try and are unsuccessful.* Now she didn't want me to write about my painful reality that extended beyond my immediate family, my *raison d'etre that* had consumed me for the last seven years. Would I allow her fear to silence me? Would I grant her that power? Was there a remote possibility that at this juncture I would be able to repress my passion about the importance of sharing this information?

I pierced the silence with a thin voice I barely recognized as my own. "I respect you and will spare you the pain. I will not mail you the letter."

Even then I continued to question whether I was prepared to rock the boat brimful with family members, some of whom I had never met. Now, what *was* my ethical responsibility? Did I have an obligation or a right to feel such responsibility? After our phone conversation, I felt like the equivocating J. Alfred Prufrock in T.S. Eliot's famous *Love Song.* Did *I dare to send the letter? Did I dare?*

All along, Larry who is all about solving problems encouraged me, saying that even though there was a chance of hostile responses from some, most will appreciate what I was doing.

Soon after the phone call, the answer came to me one Sunday afternoon while talking to a young cousin who had learned that I had written a letter and was trying to decide whether to send it. She had a one-year old with congenital myotonic dystrophy, the very worst form. My cousin had 350 CTG repeats, the same as Hunter. She had had difficulty conceiving, and finally with extensive fertility intervention, she gave birth to a child with over 3000 repeats. The hypotonic infant could not breathe or swallow at birth and was put on a feeding tube and ventilator.

She said, "I'm calling to tell you to *send the letter. You must.* It will not be easy to read, but the family needs to know."

Reassured by her encouragement, I revised the letter one more time. The next day I slid into the driver's seat, sat up straight and, gripping the steering wheel tightly with both hands, drove to the post office. With the bag of letters slung over my shoulder I climbed the steps two at a time and, with unequivocal resolve, dropped fifty-five letters into the mail slot. They were addressed to every family member of my generation and older, with the exception of one relative.

The letter went like this:

February 28, 1997

Dear Hunter relatives,

I am writing to you out of an ethical dilemma. Seven and a half years ago my now twenty-year-old son, Hunter, was diagnosed with myotonic dystrophy, a multisystemic, genetic disease that runs in the Hunter family. Helen Hunter, and Athalie and her daughter had this disease in its rather severe form. Shortly after the gene was discovered on chromosome nineteen, my now fifteen-year-old son, Ashby, and I were diagnosed with it through DNA analysis at the University of Alabama Medical School in Birmingham.

My dilemma is that I have learned a lot about this disease and feel it would be unethical for me not to convey some of this information to my relatives whose offspring, or future offspring, may be at risk. If someone had known what I now know when I was starting my family twenty years ago and had not informed me, I would be angry. But, of course, this information was not available then. I understand that some of you might not want to know about it now and "Let nature take its course," as it were. If you share this feeling, I suggest you read no further.

For those of us beyond childbearing years, the information can perhaps shed light on puzzling aspects of our own lives, or our children's, or it can be inconsequential—except to our children, grandchildren, and subsequent generations. My mother (Bash Miller) had the gene, much to the dismay of her neurologists, two of whom told me, "She does not have myotonic dystrophy; she has Parkinson's." But with her permission, I had her DNA analyzed at UAB anyway, and she did in fact have myotonic dystrophy (along with Parkinson's). A neurologist in Atlanta said to me, "Who knows? The myotonic dystrophy gene could possibly have triggered the Parkinson's." Knowing this about Momma explained a couple of symptoms that were not Parkinson's related.

New in genetic findings over the last few years is the discovery that, as some genes are passed to subsequent generations, certain parts replicate too many times and the symptoms become more pronounced with earlier onset. Simply stated, the disease often gets worse as it passes from one generation to the next. Everyone has this gene (called the DMPK gene), and up to thirty-seven CTG chemical repeats is considered normal. If one has more than fifty repeats, he has the disease. My mother had 100, I have 167, my fifteen-year old son 182, and my twenty-year old son 350; my husband, Larry, has less than 37, within the normal range.

Myotonic dystrophy is autosomal dominant, which means if one parent has it (regardless of gender) the children (regardless of gender) have a fifty-fifty chance of inheriting it. In other words, if you have the genetic mutation, you have the disease, although you might not realize you have it because your symptoms are so mild.

Myotonic dystrophy is considered a multisystemic disease. Yes, it is a degenerative muscle disease, a type of muscular dystrophy, beginning in the head and neck, hands, and sometimes feet and lower legs. However, one need not display muscle symptoms in order to have it. Those mildly affected may have only cataracts, premature balding in men or myotonia in the hands (myotonia is the inability of voluntary muscles to release on command after being tightened, as in shaking a hand or gripping a pencil). Other symptoms can be found in the cardiac, respiratory, endocrine, gastrointestinal, skeletal, and central nervous systems. More specifically, there can be speech and learning problems, reproductive difficulties, reduced initiative, lethargy, apathetic temperament, adverse reactions to anesthesia, congenital heart defects, arrhythmias, depression, anxiety, gall bladder problems, watery eyes, difficulty in swallowing, diarrhea and/or constipation, mental disorders, insulin resistance, and excessive daytime sleepiness or any perplexing combination of the above, plus additional symptoms not mentioned here. An important reason for knowing whether you have the disease, even in the mildest form, is that general anesthesia can be risky. Voluntary surgery is discouraged.

Genetic counseling is now advisable for those at risk who are getting married or starting families. Remember, a mildly affected woman can give birth to a severely affected infant. The disease is detectable through amniocentesis early in a pregnancy. If the fetus is severely affected, abortion is a possibility for some, though, I'm aware, not a consideration for others. Here we get into the question of eugenics and trying to weed out the abnormalities in the human race... But who knows? One day genetic engineering might be available, or some other form of treatment. There is current research in the field, but at present DNA analysis and careful family planning are all that are available.

Believe me: Learning this truth is a heavy burden to bear. I became deeply depressed for about three years when it was first diagnosed. But I moved through (the only preposition with integrity) the painful process of coming to grips with the diagnosis and eventually re-entering the world of the living. I was dealt a hand and not a very good one at that. But it's the only hand I'll get. I've finally found peace in accepting what I cannot change. From time to time, I find myself riding the wave of sadness, but I always reach shore and keep going. I now try to create — or grab onto — the little joys that come along, and I probably lead a more fulfilling life than I did before. Yes, there is life after diagnosis. It's not so much a matter of what comes our way, but rather how we deal with it that's critical.

Being only mildly affected, I have lived a normal, active life, dealing with occasional symptoms as they appear (some that others without this abnormal gene may also have), not knowing for years that they were possibly caused by this one defective gene. I probably would never have known I had it had Hunter not displayed more overt symptoms that triggered my curiosity. But even he has graduated from an independent, college-preparatory high school, is currently attending a local college and working at my husband's office. He has had a driver's license for six months and seems to be doing well behind the wheel. He has a very sweet disposition and is pleasant to have around most of the time. Ashby has learning problems. He does not have quite as much stamina as his peers, but he is a very social being and an avid soccer player. It is truly the next generation that concerns me: That is my primary impetus for writing this letter since we now have the ability to be proactive in preventing severe cases from being born.

If you're interested in discussing this subject further, please feel free to contact me. DNA analysis is available at UAB. The University adheres to its confidentiality policy: no one at UAB will discuss your results with anyone other than you (nor anyone else's except with them). Some of our family members have shared with me that they've been tested and found to be positive and others negative. Please mention your connection to the Hunter family so you can be added to the Hunter Study. The EMG test is NOT foolproof in detecting this disease. It revealed that I did not have the disease seven and a half years ago (because I exhibited no myotonia). (Blood can now be drawn at your internist's office for the DNA test.)

I can only imagine how some of you might be feeling if you have read this far: about the information I've presented and about me, the messenger, especially if you are hearing it for the very first

time. This is not easy information to swallow. I know only too
well.

I am mailing this to a large number of people in the Hunter
family. However, I might not be able to find all the addresses,
so share it with close relatives I might have missed. I am sending it to very few born after 1960, so you can share it with your
children as you see fit. Suggestion: If the oldest in a family line
tests negative, the younger generations need not worry. But if he
tests positive, then the next generation might then be tested, etc.
However, if it is not feasible for the oldest to take the test, then
the next generation can be tested. Some of you might want to
hold off until your children or grandchildren reach marrying age.
And I know some might elect to do nothing at all.

I hate more than you can imagine being the bearer of this
news. It has taken me a long time to have the courage to write
this letter. The knowledge of this disease has pointed up that even
though I've never met some of you, we are inextricably bound
through this gene, and through thousands of other genes like hair
and eye color and a multitude of other wonderful ways. I've even
gotten to meet some of you for the first time because of the gene.

Some researchers strongly suspect that Monet had myotonic
dystrophy that caused cataracts that gradually clouded his vision.
So, our disease was the springboard for Impressionism! There is a
silver lining in even the darkest clouds.

Again, please contact me if you feel inclined.

My love to each of you on Marian Macpherson's Hunter tree,

Your cousin, Shannon Miller Lord

(Third child of Marian Shannon Ross and Harold Crenshaw
Miller)

After mailing the letters, I questioned how people would re-act to receiving the information. Would they be angry? Would they be afraid? Would they put their heads in the sand? Like my father, the consummate engineer and stickler for details, would have no doubt done, I calculated the percentage. Over the next month or two I heard from sixty-five per cent of the recipients with messages like these:

> "Thank you so much for your letter. I really do believe knowledge is the best defense. Thank you on behalf of my side of the family for your thorough study of the disease and your willingness to share it and teach us."

> "Thank you so very much for your interest, trouble, and most of all courage in compiling and sending the vital information about myotonic dystrophy. This branch of the Hunter family feels you have done a noble act to enlighten all of us at risk and also a ser-vice to future generations. I'm sure you have profoundly disturbed some of us and I'm sure you have had some unpleasant feedback from those who prefer to be blind."

So far so good. These relatives *appreciated* the information.

> "It is quite clear that my father suffered from the disease, and it probably contributed materially to his death at age 52. In childhood, he had suffered from gastrointestinal problems, and his physical condition prevented him from successfully participating in the sports he loved. He suffered from a weak grip that won him a medical discharge from the infantry in World War II. My

father slept an inordinate amount, and had cataracts before he was 50. He reportedly suffered heart failure under anesthesia during the cataract operation. Revived, he survived a couple of years of declining health until a heart attack killed him soon after his fifty-second birthday. I do not think his disease was ever correctly diagnosed. It was clear that he was ill, but no one seemed to know what the problem was. Your letter should be very helpful to those who receive it. All the Hunters that I see from time to time have seen it, but I cannot really tell what their reaction is."

This cousin too was appreciative of the information. His observations about his father made more sense now that he knew about the disease. But not too many relatives were as effusive in their responses. And, as the above message indicates, the information in the letter was seldom a topic of conversation. Notes continued to dribble in and finally this one arrived from my cousin, Susan Tucker.

"One of the silver linings, which I know is indeed small recompense, is that your letter does indeed explain so much to all of us about ourselves. And I thank you for that. I write because I appreciate your courage, and want to respond in kind.

My aunt probably had myotonic dystrophy. One day my step-grandmother said to me many years after my aunt's death, 'You know, there was something wrong with [your aunt].'

"'A heart disease,' I replied.

"My step-grandmother paused for a long time, as if she were considering what to tell me. I thought she couldn't remember, but now I think differently. She said, 'She was a little retarded; she could not speak well.'

"I have my aunt's books—many of them—I know she was not retarded. She read. She also made scrapbooks. I have some of these. I became an archivist because I was interested in the records she left us, and of course, in the records of others, our shared history.

"I stayed with Granny [Susan's biological grandmother and my own great aunt] often. She liked to garden. Every day when I was there, we would go into the garden and she would say to me (at least this is how it seemed to me), 'Every little seed will not be a perfect flower.' I always knew that this was important to her and even as a child, I knew that this statement told me not only not to wish for perfection, but also held some heavier weight and sorrow I couldn't identify. And in the end, this desire to present a daily placement of oneself within nature's imperfection, well, this explains disease. It does so rather nobly and without embellishment.

"All these are small legacies, a little recompense for the sorrow you feel. I want you to know that I would like to help. Shall we do something more? What can I do? Can we have a family reunion and raise money for research? Can we do something fun like go to Scotland? And would you like to see the photographs I have?

With gratitude, sincerity, and kinship."

I knew of Susan but had never met her in person, and yet she was someone with whom I was closely connected genetically and with whom I felt immediate kinship. She was an archivist and writer herself, and, best of all, she was willing to embrace the greater family truth, to stand with us, not separate from us. I re-read her letter a number of times, then and in the ensuing years and was always comforted and moved by her depth of insight and empathy.

I have wondered how the other thirty-five per cent of my relatives reacted to my letter. Although no one openly berated me, there were probably those who would have liked to, or were disturbed, if not devastated, to receive such a missive. Some of them never acknowledged receiving it. Perhaps they filed the letters in dark recesses of silence and hoped to forget they were there, or better, threw them away. One cousin said she glanced at it hurriedly. "Oh, Sha! I put it in my bank box; maybe I'll have my children tested before they get married."

On her birthday the following summer, I called the relative who had reacted vehemently to my sending the letter. During our conversation, once again the subject of myotonic dystrophy came up. I stated that I did *not* want any pity, that I was doing quite well, and that I had finally come to accept the hand we were dealt. I remember confidently repeating my sentiment: *I do not want any pity.*

The next day she called and announced emphatically that she wanted to make a contribution to myotonic dystrophy research; she wanted the address before the end of the day. For the first time, I heard her say the words *myotonic dystrophy.* At least for the moment she had transcended her paralyzing fear. I perceived her courage and enthusiasm and her request for an address as permission and encouragement to forge ahead.

Thus, I embarked on a new odyssey that would guide the rest of my life. This time, however, it was not just Larry and me trying desperately to learn "what was wrong" with both of our boys and to find the right "fix" for them. Now we were joined by many members of the Hunter clan that lived up to the honor bestowed on them by King David I. Just as William put his expertise to good use in the wild forests and fens that surrounded a fort that later became Hunter's Toun, we were determined to pursue resources to support research on myotonic dystrophy and the development of treatments for those suffering from it. Our faulty gene may have begun in the forests of Hunterston, as it is now called, so it seemed natural that we would seek answers with the same tenacity that produced hunters and soldiers of distinction over the generations.

Yet, even as I stepped fearfully and joyfully into my new role and became an activist, fundraiser, and public speaker, my life was punctuated by many heartbreaking reminders of the toll that DM continued to take on all our descendant family, my sons in particular.

11. Mobilizing the Family

Our seven-year diagnostic odyssey and ensuing frustrations with finding informed practitioners had made it crystal clear that most doctors, educators, and counselors knew little about this rare disease. Families like ours endured considerable anxiety and frustration in long, drawn-out diagnostic journeys that often lasted for years, all the while knowing in our guts and hearts that something *was not quite right.* Sometimes we were given incorrect diagnoses or made to believe the behavior in question was a result of bad parenting.

Even after we received a correct diagnosis, we encountered more frustration because there were limited resources for education and a lack of understanding, validation, and support from the medical profession. We understood that these disappointing responses were caused by lack of knowledge and experience to recognize and treat this disease. Yet, many teachers, counselors, and doctors dismissed our efforts to educate them about DM. For example, the professionals at Ashby's treatment center in New York openly admitted they knew nothing about DM except what

Ashby had taught them. At the request of Ashby's counselor, I mailed them a 67-page report along with three psychological evaluations administered at ages eight, fourteen, and nineteen. His evaluations revealed consistent symptoms, including anxiety that he had exhibited since the tender age of eight—long before his use of drugs and alcohol. In spite of my efforts to provide this information, the professionals at the treatment center were not receptive to my offerings. I heard one mumble under his breath about my attempts to micro-manage.

This response may have been the pivotal moment when I stopped being intimidated by such comments and committed myself to becoming an advocate, a role that would become my life's mission. By now I had learned a lot about the disease, and I knew that I could make a contribution. I started on the next phase of my crusade with a deep and earnest passion.

As Cousin Susan had suggested in her thoughtful letter, organizing a family gathering would bring the Hunter Clan together for rekindling family relationships, increasing awareness of our family disease, and raising money for research into its causes and in order to discover treatments. The majority of descendants of the Hunters who settled in the Mobile area 120 years earlier still lived there. Susan, several other cousins, and I began stirring interest and planning the event. Most of our communication took place by e-mail. This new means of communication cut through time and space with thrilling immediacy to reach people wherever they were in the world, without having to know their physical location.

Susan created and printed a detailed family history and genealogy for everyone. Her vibrant, driving spirit energized and propelled the process. A retired engineer, also named Shannon, worked diligently on a family history power-point presentation, another new invention that ran continuously throughout the afternoon. Howard, an octogenarian and retired advertising executive, filled in many blanks by taking photographs of old family homes and unearthing other pictures and bits of family history in the archives at the University of South Alabama.

Over a hundred and eighty Hunter relatives showed up for the event on a beautiful fall Saturday afternoon in November of 1997. Various ones helped with hors d'hoeuvres, box lunches, drinks, Highland games for the young Scottish descendants, bag pipes playing, decorations, parking, and clean-up. The Civil War hospital-turned-church retreat was transformed into a Scottish banquet hall on the shore of Mobile Bay. To raise money, we had an auction that included original works of art, autographed books by family members, and the use of houses in New Orleans and Telluride. I donated one of my hand-painted game tables and a pair of chairs. Golf paraphernalia were popular auction items, reflecting the heritage of our family patriarch who built the first golf course in Mobile in 1897 because he missed the game he had played as a youth in Scotland. In spite of the Hunters' penurious Scottish reputation, we raised $8,500 that crystalline day on Mobile Bay.

People understood why we were having the auction and gave generously. However, a tacit agreement to avoid mentioning "the elephant in the room" also prevailed. *The words "myotonic dystrophy" were never mentioned publically the entire afternoon!*

After the family gathering, Howard, now nearly ninety, recapped the event in an e-mail. *"Some Food [sic] Notes from the*

gathering: Venetia [his daughter and organizer of the children's High-
land Games] had a dozen boiled eggs for the egg roll, but some male
fugitive from Ritalin stomped them all!"

In spite of this impulsive act, the day proved hugely successful
on many levels. We as a family had finally come together in an
unspoken acknowledgement of our family disease and had joined
to raise money for research.

As we knew that the disease was one of the muscular dystrophies, I had contacted the Muscular Dystrophy Association
(MDA) because I needed a tax-deductible organization where
donors could send their checks. They were willing to receive the
contributions but also told me that myotonic dystrophy was not
a priority for their funding. However, they assured me that we
could send in the money and designate the recipient for this
modest sum of research money and no overhead would be de-
ducted for this service. The next question was: to whom should
we send the money? Who were the leaders in research?

Thus began a summer of Internet surfing, a welcomed and
newly available tool although still in its infancy in 1997. How
could I, an English major who had avoided all science courses
since high school biology, get involved with medical research? I
couldn't fix my children or myself, but perhaps I could interface
with those who might one day develop a treatment. So, I started
contacting everyone I knew who was involved in research of any
sort.

First, I invited Dr. Krawiecki—the pediatric neurologist who
had diagnosed Hunter correctly—to lunch at his favorite French
restaurant. I fired questions at him, one after another about what
I could do to work with the research community. He said fund-

raising would be an important first step but acknowledged that it was not something he did well. However, he encouraged me to continue fundraising and said that he was confident I would be successful.

Next, I turned to Larry's first cousin, John Moseley, a former physicist at Stanford Research Institute and then Director of Research and ultimately Provost at the University of Oregon. He introduced me to Dave Frohnmayer, President of the University and his wife Lynn who had started the Fanconi Anemia Research Fund to support research on their inherited family disorder. On a visit with John and his family, his wife Susan took me to meet Dave and Lynn Frohnmayer. After describing my situation, which was not dissimilar to theirs, they told me their story. They described their success in bringing together researchers and physicians to share what they knew and where their research was headed. They, of course, mentioned fundraising as critical to these efforts. Dave then asked, "Do you have a registry? That's very important."

"A *what?*" I was almost too embarrassed to ask what that was. I soon learned that a registry is an organized system for the collection, storage, retrieval, analysis, and dissemination of information on individuals who have a particular disease. So, now I wondered how could I get that going or if there was one already in existence. I later discovered that the University of Rochester Medical Center had started a DM registry funded by the NIH. I made sure that those with the disease that I contacted knew to submit their information to the registry.

I increasingly realized that I had much to learn about being an advocate for research. How could I begin to understand the way doctors and researchers (or investigators, I learned they are called) worked? Are they secretive, working solo into the night hoping to win the next grant or Nobel Prize? Or are they collaborative, willing to share research data, knowledge, and wisdom as well as mice and tissue samples?

Should I try to endow a chair at a medical school as one doctor suggested?

Should I start a non-profit foundation?

Should I instigate a brainstorming session among DM investigators?

Have investigators studying a range of genetic disorders caused by similar defects ever met and collaborated? Would such a gathering be helpful?

I asked these questions and many more to all with whom I came in contact in the medical field as I tried to flesh out a picture that made sense.

That summer in 1998, six months after the Hunter family gathering, I printed a stack of myotonic dystrophy articles I found on the Internet from the Muscular Dystrophy Association, the National Institutes of Health, and various medical schools. I skimmed the articles and circled names I saw repeatedly like Moxley, Thornton, and Ashizawa, the investigators whose postage-stamp-sized photos embellished the studies. I printed and placed them in manila folders then put the folders in my gray metal file cabinet. All I knew now was that I was challenged by something that had landed unasked-for on my door step, something I desperately needed to understand. Perhaps it is a legacy of my father, but I have always needed to know *why* something is so. Now I was impassioned and driven by a greater goal that I trusted one day would come into full focus. At the same time, I wondered if I would ever get to meet these experts in the field and whether I would be able to carry on an intelligent conversation with them if I did. I had communicated with Dr. Harper several times since first meeting him. Now I sought his advice again: *To whom should we channel the money?* Better than anyone else, he had his finger on the pulse of DM research.

He replied, "Thank you for writing about myotonic dystrophy. It is good to know how successful your efforts have been. In the U.S., I would suggest Dr. Tetsuo Ashizawa at Baylor College of Medicine as a worthy recipient." Suddenly, I could visualize a postage-stamp sized image of a youthful looking neurologist with intense eyes and a compelling smile. In the gray files filled with the results of my summer of Internet surfing I found his photograph, biography, and titles of his published papers on myotonic dystrophy.

At my request, the MDA forwarded the $8,500 to Dr. Ashizawa for myotonic dystrophy research. Almost immediately, Tom Moore, the Development Director at Baylor, called to say he was delighted with the news from the MDA. He offered to start a separate account for myotonic dystrophy research with Dr. Ashizawa as steward. Tom expressed enthusiasm and appreciation for my efforts while exerting no pressure on how much money I raised now or in the future. And so, the *Hunter Research Fund* was born. Months later, after frequent e-mail exchanges, Tom told me that one of the most rewarding parts of his job is watching a donor and investigator bond, a reminder to him of the importance of human connection.

Very soon, I fell into regular e-mail communication with Dr.

Ashizawa who insisted I call him "Tee". From the Frohnmayers at the University of Oregon I had learned that their annual
brainstorming session for investigators had been the best use of
their money to date. In less than a week after mentioning this
idea to Tee, he had e-mailed the DM researchers who would be
attending the American Society for Human Genetics meeting in
Philadelphia in October 2000, and invited them to attend a small
discussion session during the conference then join us for drinks
and a buffet dinner afterwards.

Once the money raised at the family gathering was in Tee's
hands, the events leading to this genetics conference were
straight-forward and smooth. My goals were beginning to come
into focus out of a foggy notion and gut-level need to know *why*
and to *do something* to move research along: communicating with
investigators, helping them understand the nuances of this complex, multi-systemic disease, and contributing to their research
since they were the ones who, if anyone could, might develop a
treatment for our family disorder.

On October 5, 2000, twenty-five investigators from Europe and North America—from the venerable Dr. Harper to a
first-time presenter, Mario Pereira, a young Portuguese scientist
at the University of Glasgow—convened in a dimly-lit conference room and discussed their most recent research. Collaboration took place before our eyes. "You have four patients—he has
two—and I have three. Maybe we can work together..."

First-hand, I observed the mutual respect that Tee had described as essential for successful collaboration. I could detect
contagious determination, passion, and synergy mounting as the
evening wore on. Larry and I, and the boys, who were nineteen

and twenty-four at the time, exchanged awed glances during the presentations. At one point, Ashby asked for pen and paper to jot down questions for later.

Prior to the conference, Tee had asked me to speak briefly. At the conclusion of the presentations, as light magically refilled the room, I walked to the front with my insides aflutter. Before me sat twenty-five DM investigators, some whose tiny photos lay in manila files next to Tee's. I introduced our family and revealed that both boys and I had myotonic dystrophy and reported our number of CTG repeats. I told them about how my family had raised a modest amount of money for research and how I had learned about and found Tee. I continued, "I believe I can speak for my family and myself: we did not comprehend a lot of what you said tonight. I heard repeated references to *exon* and *bp* that have always meant something very different to me. But we are eternally indebted to you for choosing this area of research as part of your life's work. Now, let's have dinner in the next room."

As soon as I finished speaking, over half of the investigators descended on me and the boys to say that in all their years of research, *they had never met a person, let alone a family, with myotonic dystrophy.* This revelation remains my most vivid memory of our trip to Philadelphia.

But this was not all that transpired that night.

12. Fundraising

Talking to my younger brother David in early August of 2000, two months before the October meeting in Philadelphia, I mentioned that I was contemplating a letter-writing campaign to friends and family to raise additional money for myotonic dystrophy research. The Frohnmayers had assured me a couple of years earlier that fundraising would be an important part of my advocacy work. David encouraged me to write and mail the letter now so that the money could be presented to Tee at the meeting in Philadelphia.

The meeting was less than two months away, but I usually operate best with a deadline, and immediately set about writing a letter. By this time, things were not as good in Hunter's life as they had been three years earlier when I wrote to our extended family about the disease. After his grand mal seizure, car wrecks, and lack of success pursuing college any further, he was now working at Larry's architectural firm full time. Ashby, on the other hand, had graduated from high school and was about to start college — a positive transition on the surface. However, we had many concerns about how well he would manage his new independent environment. A few days before the conference, Larry had brought Ashby home from college.

In late August, I mailed 450 letters asking for financial support for myotonic dystrophy research. I couldn't help but wonder how many people would reply. How much money could we possibly raise? I had never attempted anything like this before, but I enjoyed writing letters and making a connection with an intended recipient. I knew I had come a long way when I wrote the first sentence. A few excerpts from the letter are below:

August 20, 2000

Dear _____,

I am writing to ask for your help.

… Hunter no longer drives and will require some sort of care always. Ashby is despairing over symptoms that are slowly appearing as he prepares to start college.

Last fall, my family initiated a fund-raising effort…channeled the money to Dr. Tetsuo Ashizawa and started the Hunter Research Fund at Baylor College of Medicine. According to the author of the definitive work on the disorder, "He is one of the people with the most expertise in both the clinical and research aspects and also a very concerned and caring clinician."

It took me several years to arrive at a place emotionally where I could finally accept the hand we were dealt. But…I have learned that the best form of defense is offense; hence, this letter asking for your support.

Thank you in advance for your consideration.

With grateful appreciation,
Shannon Lord

As I was writing the letter I wondered just how much we might actually raise. Larry, a veteran fund-raiser for other causes, advised me to shoot high: Ask for more than you think you'll get and expect it. As my nerves calmed to the idea of asking for contributions, I crossed out $30,000 and stated that I was shooting for *$200,000*—enough to cover an entire project for 2-3 years. And what would happen if we didn't reach the goal? It would reduce the research and collaboration that could be done but other than that ... nothing.

I nervously mailed the letters, sat back, and waited.

The first donation arrived in our mailbox four days later from a young, newly married Hunter cousin. I was deeply moved knowing I would not have been as magnanimous at that age.

Each day I walked up our long driveway through the woods to the mailbox. Several contributors, with whom I had had only a single conversation, were extraordinarily generous. And along with the checks came letters, notes, e-mails, and phone calls.

"When your letter came originally it stirred so many emotions. Anger and sadness at hearing Ashby is also affected, awe of your strength (a true mother lion) and action..."

"I have thought about your letter and thought about your letter and it hurts so much to think about it. There is such sadness now that envelops all my happy memories of your parents, whom I loved, of your brothers and sister and you and your family. You are a brave, wonderful woman, Shannon, a true inheritor of all the wonderful character that was in both of your parents…"

"I have reread your letter of August 20 and once again I weep for you and Hunter and Ashby and Larry. It is too easy to get caught up in our own family issues and comings and goings and close our eyes to those we care about — even just down the street. We feel honored and privileged to join you in your efforts…"

"I have been so moved by your letter — and your note to us. Just wanted to write a personal line or two from me, to say that throughout all the struggling years you and your boys have been so deep in our hearts, I think I understand a little more about myotonic dystrophy now — and so grateful we can help. You are quite a lady!"

"You have truly led in this effort — I am just amazed, and very proud of you. [We] are pleased to be able to help out in the cause… I'll try not to make this too weepy, knowing what the daily mailbox experience is like these days. But you get our award for 'Best Fund-raiser' — perhaps this should be a new career. Much love…"

"You're on the right track!!! I thought your letter was very enlightening and very appropriate. These curves don't just happen to other people…they seem to happen to all of us, but in different ways. These are character-building experiences. I have every confidence that you are a "chosen one" and that you will make a difference. Good luck, and never quit asking for help, until the monster is eradicated!!!"

I had never considered the nature of the messages that would arrive with the contributions, every one different from the next but alike at the same time, and all felt like a soothing balm. Each day as I read the notes on my way back through the woods to the house, I wept with appreciation and humility. Totally unaware, I was blindsided with love.

As well as contacting family members, I also mailed the letter to Irene Diamond, the Founder and Director of the Aaron Diamond Fund in New York City. Larry knew her because his architectural firm had designed the Aaron Diamond AIDS Research Center that she had funded. A few days later, she called Larry. Larry told me the receptionist at his office had paged him and then transferred the call to a phone where he was standing in the lobby of the office. Mrs. Diamond acknowledged receipt of my letter and reminded him that her foundation funded medical research, the arts, and minority education *only* in New York City. Only on two previous occasions had her foundation given money to people in other cities.

"However," she continued, "I found Shannon's letter one of the most compelling I've ever received. And you know I get a lot. Would it work if I send her $25,000 this year and the same next year?" Larry said, "Yes, ma'am," a phrase that Mrs. Diamond said she never got tired of hearing from her southern friend.

Still standing in the middle of the lobby, Larry called me immediately. In his booming voice that must have reverberated to every corner, he told me about the call. Alone in the house I jumped up and down. We exchanged shouts of joy as we realized that we were well on the way to reaching our goal of making additional research a reality. I allowed myself time to calm down before I sat down and wrote Irene a note.

> …thank you for making such a significant imprint on the world.
>   It has become apparent to me that humankind is bonded most deeply around adversity and loss.

I was caught by surprise by the profound lesson I learned from my first solo fundraising effort: In the face of another's adversity, genuine responses of empathy and generosity can penetrate the veneer of arrogance, competitiveness, and indifference that envelopes many of us. The same response does not emerge as often in the presence of others' successes or triumphs.

Poignant memories of the previous six weeks danced in my head as I stood in the buffet line at the conclusion of the brainstorming session in Philadelphia. Tee had done a superb job of organizing and orchestrating the session. He had introduced my family and me to the world of research. In addition, he had introduced over half of the investigators present to the first DM patients they had ever met. The evening ebbed and flowed over a glass of wine and dinner with serious conversation interspersed with laughter and cheerfulness. Life had changed dramatically since I lay in a fetal position on my living room sofa, with my eyes closed, overwhelmed by depression.

At the end of the evening, as dinner drew to a close, Larry tapped his glass with a spoon to get everyone's attention. The room quieted. I stood up and described how over the last few months, I had been asking friends and relatives to help with a contribution to support medical research in myotonic dystrophy.

With that introduction, Hunter and Ashby came forward and presented Tee with a larger-than-life check for $155,000. There was loud applause and another round of handshakes, hugs, and congratulations.

The evening in Philadelphia was exhilarating. With additional letter campaigns, a little over a year later we exceeded the goal of $200,000, and the next year surpassed $250,000. In subsequent years, we raised even more. I had become an official fundraiser.

13. Participating in the World of Research

In the spring of 2001, while Ashby was in the wilderness pro-
gram, I was invited to Baylor College of Medicine to meet the
collaborators conducting research supported by the Hunter Research Fund. Larry, Hunter, and I had planned to travel to Utah
to have a family meeting with Ashby at his program, and logis-
tically, it would work well for me to stop in Houston on my way
home from that.

At that point, Ashby had been kicked out of the rehab program and was homeless in Cortez. I was reeling from his disaster
and disappointment, and I was not sure if I had the emotional
strength to visit Baylor. But when Ashby called to tell us he had
a job and a place to stay, I decided I could manage the trip to
Baylor. Although we later learned that these reassurances were
untrue, they did provide momentary relief. As I weighed my options, I realized that perhaps the trip would divert my obsessive
thoughts about Ashby. As recommended by his program, we had
attended several Nar-Anon meetings, and their message kept

playing in my head: "Do not allow your addict to destroy you. You must continue living your life." I went to Baylor as I had planned.

Over lunch at a lovely restaurant in Houston, I had the opportunity to meet several more investigators. I listened to descriptions of their planned project with transgenic mice, Drosophila, and human cells. They spoke a language foreign to me; it could just as well have been Sinhalese. They talked of trinucleotide repeats, CUGbp, SIX5, and so on. I'd come across some of these words in my readings and at the Philadelphia meeting, but I still faced a steep learning curve. One investigator explained the usual peer-review process of awarding research grants. Another spoke enthusiastically about fulfilling a dream: rowing down the Rhine after suffering heart problems and getting a pacemaker. The most junior investigator had returned a day early from a conference in California so he could join us. I found these men to be approachable and felt at ease talking to them.

During our spirited conversation at lunch, Tee, who had laryngitis, leaned over and spoke in a raspy whisper, "I - think - you - ought - to - go - to - Kyoto - with - us." Tee, along with a French colleague, had founded a biennial meeting four years earlier to create a collaborative environment that would expedite work and lead to understanding the disease mechanism and developing possible treatments. In five months, the Third Biennial International Myotonic Dystrophy Consortium (IDMC-3) was going to convene at the Miyako Hotel in Kyoto, Japan. Doctors and scientists from all over the world would present their recent findings. I was honored but at the same time uncertain as to why he had invited me. It turned out he planned to use a portion of the Hunter Research Fund to cover travel expenses for North American investigators attending the conference. In other words, I was a sponsor.

With this trip now before me, I thought back to those endless hours I spent on the sofa after our diagnosis. I recalled a quote that I had heard back then: *we all need someone to love, something to do, and something to look forward to.* I had dismissed it as trite; but now I understood it. I embraced the Kyoto trip as *something to look forward to.*

A month later I received a copied e-mail exchange between Tee and the Japanese Chairman of the conference: "We are happy to welcome Mrs. Shannon Lord," wrote the Chairman. "Her speech will be one of the most impressive events at the reception."

Immediately I e-mailed Tee, *"What speech?!"* What was I to talk about at this "prestigious event"? I called Larry right away to tell him what had happened. He was thrilled. He assured me that I would become an important part of that organization because I would be using my English major to its fullest advantage as a patient advocate.

At first I felt speech-*less*, but I quickly came to think of it as an incredible opportunity to address physicians and scientists whose names were now familiar to me. I bounced ideas off Larry and discussed travel plans, equivocating over the dates and times. Because I was traveling that far, I decided to allow a couple of extra days to explore Japan.

One night in the midst of our brainstorming, I finally settled on my travel dates. Larry still remembers exactly where we were standing in the living room when he said, "Tomorrow, I'll book your flights."

I paused for a moment to consider his offer. The irregular pattern of my life had taken me to previously unimaginable places. There were those times when I had encountered emotional walls I couldn't scale; or equivocated over decisions like whether or not to send the letter to my Hunter relatives. I had moved on from helping plan a family gathering and auction to becoming a successful fund raiser. I was now fully committed to tackling this disease. It had become my personal commitment to learn as much as I could about this aberrant mutation that resided in the DNA of Hunter, Ashby, and me. I had already been trying to educate their teachers and doctors who knew little about it. Perhaps I could even explain some of the disease's subtleties to researchers. I was impassioned by this challenge. It energized me. My pursuit had become a primary purpose for getting out of bed every day. Mothers of children with challenges of any sort can surely identify with my determination. I had a feeling that *this* was the type of purpose that feminists and Joseph Campbell, with his follow-your-bliss philosophy, had envisioned for women all those years ago. This was *my* challenge. I now *owned* it. It was mine to carry out. I was a capable, self-reliant woman in charge of myself.

Still standing in the living room with my feet now firmly planted and my arms akimbo, I responded to Larry, *"I can make the reservations myself, thank you!"*

And I did just that.

The time leading up to my trip, however, was filled with drama and uncertainty. About three weeks before my departure came the shocking 9/11 terrorist attacks on New York and Washington, DC. In an instant, on a clear, sunny, fall day, fear gripped the minds and hearts of every American. The random killing of thousands of people left the rest of us feeling devastated, helpless, and in shock. What had our world come to? How could this have happened? What would happen next? A number of DM investigators planning to go to Japan cancelled their trips. The conference was obviously going to be smaller than planned, but it was still going to take place.

Then, three days before I was scheduled to leave for Japan, we received the fateful call that Ashby was being kicked out of the life skills program in Bend, Oregon and was now homeless.

Larry and I discussed Ashby's latest crisis and whether or not I should go to Japan but kept reminding ourselves of the advice learned at Nar-Anon just as I had when trying to decide about my trip to Baylor.

Ashby would have to deal with the consequences of his latest actions. I must go on with my life. I knew I had to go. And 9/11 was not going to deter me either.

Ashby knew I was planning to go to Japan. By the time he called back several hours later, I was braced for the call and answered on the first ring. "Ashby, I'm still going to Japan in three days. You'll have to fend for yourself."

"That's good. Don't stay home because of me. You know: I'm a survivor." In the midst of trying to detach with love and practice tough love as addiction groups advise, I detected a false bravado in his voice. I had heard it before. I faltered for a moment but not long enough to change my mind.

Upon arrival in Kyoto, the Japanese organizers introduced me to a beautiful, slender, young Japanese woman named Takako who had been assigned to take care of me during the conference. She was the wife of an endocrinologist, a leading researcher of myotonic dystrophy in Osaka; she spoke English and had agreed to look after me during the conference. I didn't think I needed a caretaker. After all, I had made my own reservations, flown from Atlanta by myself, and had managed quite well. Ultimately, I assumed this was the Japanese way and accepted her caretaking graciously.

On the first day, I broke my glasses and was thankful to have her accompany me to Takashimaya to buy new frames. As I tried on each pair she would wrinkle her nose and shake her head, or wince, or laugh. "No, they make you look like old lady!" "Oh no! Too shiny!" Until finally, we reached consensus on a simple pair that would get the job done. Takako was a wonderfully warm and generously supportive person. As it turned out, we thoroughly enjoyed each other's company, and I did not feel that her help in any way diminished my new-found mission, strength and courage.

A couple of mornings after my arrival, I awoke in my hotel room and turned on CNN. With a cup of coffee in my hand, I stepped onto my balcony outlined with yellow and orange marigolds and gazed at the rooftops of the beautiful city of Kyoto and the mountains beyond. My senses were heightened because I had made it here at all. I simply stood there absorbing every aspect of the morning. This sublime moment was interrupted by the TV announcer's voice that wafted through the sheer curtain undulating in the open door, *"The U.S. has invaded Afghanistan…"*

I could hardly take it in. My country was at war.

Ashby was homeless.

And I was an invited speaker at an international meeting in Japan. In fact, I was the *only* invited attendee with myotonic dystrophy.

The surreal juxtaposition of circumstances that converged on me in Kyoto that clear, crisp October morning, will remain with me forever.

At the end of the first day of meetings, the researchers and I convened in the ballroom of the hotel for the reception that was in truth a seven-course banquet with performing Maiko girls (or teenage geishas in-training). With chalky white faces, traditional kimonos, sculpted black hair, and high wooden shoes, they danced, sang, played musical instruments, and hovered round our tables while laughing, pouring sake, and helping move conversation along.

One course consisted of a small, hand-woven seaweed basket and in it a tiny, round, red and white checkerboard created from raw fish surrounded by a band of seaweed. It was a visual and gustatory feast, executed in true Japanese form, or *kata*, a meal of absolute perfection and my most memorable dining experience ever.

After the last course and an introduction, I made my way to the front to speak to this international audience. Fortunately, English is the designated language of these meetings, but I was struck that the majority of those in attendance were experiencing the entire conference in a second language. I gripped the lectern, gazed out at a sea of faces and began to speak.

"Many years ago, my husband's cousin, a physicist at Stanford Research Institute and later the Provost at the University of Oregon, wondered each time he read a paper published by a particular physicist what M.H. Fellow meant after his name. Other investigators in the room had been fellows of some sort; but no one in that highly esteemed intelligentsia was familiar with that particular fellowship, and no one dared to ask. Finally after several published papers, one curious person finally harnessed his courage: "What is an M.H. Fellow?" to which the physicist replied, "A Most Happy Fellow!"… In search of credentials for my attendance at this consortium and with no PhD's or MD's to follow my name, I realized I could honestly say: I am a Most Happy Fellow to be here. Unlike you, I can write after my name 167 CTG Repeats and offer a DM patient's perspective on the disease.

"I present with cataracts, a goiter, and the need for a lot of sleep. I have had a parotidectomy and anesthesia complications. I had difficulty conceiving and delivering both of my children, and had a miscarriage between the two. After reading Peter Harper's book, I realize all these to be manifestations of the disease. It was odd then that when an EMG was administered, it revealed no myotonia. I might never have known I have the disorder had I not observed this insidious gene working in aberrant ways in my older son. In the early '90's, after some of you in this room located the DM gene on Chromosome 19, my younger son was diagnosed with it also. Tonight, I want to talk briefly about my family, life after diagnosis, and most importantly, about you.

"As I think about my ancestors who came to America from Scotland and Northern Ireland in the 1880's, I see this disease manifesting itself in myriad ways in their descendants: lethargy, cataracts, complications from anesthesia, holes in the heart, GI problems, premature balding, sleepiness, heart problems, several early deaths, and others. From observing various branches of my family, I would say six out of seven of my grandmother's siblings inherited the DM gene. Having learned a lot about the disorder, I have wrestled with my ethical responsibility to my family. Several years ago, I wrote a letter offering information about the disease, and since then have learned that it is a difficult topic for most people to discuss.

"My 25-year-old son, Hunter, has 350 repeats. He lives with us and works in my husband's architectural office as a helper. He needs to be awakened every morning by my husband or me. He has struggled with learning disabilities, inattention, poor socialization, myotonia, digestive problems, choking, and minimal muscle wasting—so far. He has the classic myotonic dystrophy look with an open mouth, droopy eyelids, and a blunt affect. Though standardized tests reveal a 125-130 IQ, he meshes comfortably into a social group of adults with developmental disabilities. He is enthusiastic about baseball and the stock market. He has a generous spirit and has contributed several hundred dollars of his own money to myotonic dystrophy research. In his naïveté and general aloofness, he does not question his life. On the contrary, he is quite content.

"My other son, Ashby, who is now 20, has 182 trinucleotide repeats. Although he appears to be less affected than his brother and was a good soccer player in school, he is utterly distraught because of the disease. Like his brother, he has learning difficulties and attention problems. I also wonder if his musculature, skeletal make-up, and mental processing are adversely affected. Just a few weeks ago he tearfully admitted that he always felt stupid in school from the very beginning when he tried to learn how to read. He is much more socially adept than his brother and more aware of the possible disease manifestations for himself. At

age 15 he started smoking pot and is now wrestling with marijuana dependency. For several years, we've questioned how much
of his behavior is caused by marijuana abuse, myotonic dystrophy,
or normal adolescence—or a combination.

"My husband, Larry, bounces out of bed every morning at 5,
works at his computer until he awakens Hunter at 6:30. About 12
years ago he started his own architectural firm, which now numbers over a hundred people, and ironically designs many medical
school research laboratories. Super-endowed with energy and
passion, he has been extremely active in the community, affairs
like Leadership Atlanta, a homeless shelter, a large downtown
church. He has raised money from foundations to build a youth
soccer complex and tries to stay young by running up and down
those fields with black shorts and a whistle around his neck. He's
a bit ADHD himself, but he channels it to his advantage. The
reality is that he cannot do just one thing at a time. He could have
bolted a long time ago, but he has slowly honed his patience over
the years and hung in there with the three of us. He and I almost
always pull together where the children are involved…And, yes,
you guessed it. He has fewer than 37 CTG repeats.

"Our journey has been long and frustrating, and I am taken
aback when I hear DM referred to as a neuromuscular disease,
because it is so much more. The psychosocial and emotional aspects of DM have plagued our family, thus far, more significantly
than the physical ones. This is still a little understood disorder,
even among doctors attempting to treat us. We searched for sev-
en years to find a correct diagnosis. We saw a highly respected
pediatric neurologist when Hunter was six, who laughed at us
and assured us nothing was wrong. When Hunter was twelve,

a psychiatrist diagnosed him as a childhood schizophrenic. Immediately, we sought a second opinion from a neurologist who diagnosed Hunter with myotonic dystrophy, in ten minutes. Because I have found very few other doctors in Atlanta who truly understand the disease, I have taken Professor Harper's book to many doctors' appointments to try and teach them.

"Now, I'd like to shift to life after diagnosis. Anna Quindlen, American author and Pulitzer Prize winner, who lost her mother to cancer at age nineteen, writes in A Short Guide to a Happy Life: "Knowledge of our mortality is the greatest gift [we ever receive], because unless you know the clock is ticking, it is so easy to waste our days, our lives." She writes about her mother's death: "It was the dividing line between seeing the world in black and white, and in Technicolor. The lights came on for the darkest possible reason...

"After Hunter's diagnosis, even though I firmly believed I would never experience another moment's joy in my life, finally, I began to see light at the top of the black hole into which I had fallen. My life will forever be divided into life before and after diagnosis.

"The 17th century French philosopher, Rene Descartes, wrote about the metaphysical split, or dualism, of mind and body. Western doctors came to treat the body without consideration for the mind and spirit, all of which must be addressed if any healing is to take place. There are several key factors that helped me emerge from those dark days of despair and hopelessness: deep human connection, a sense of control over my attitude, the importance of art, and a sense of humor.

"Deep human connection. In a therapy group, the revelation

of my truths in the face of other people who listened well, and my willingness to go through my pain and fears and not skirt around them eventually helped the sadness to wane. Although my sons and I still have the disease, I am able to live with more purpose, focus, and passion than before.

"Sometime during this slow healing process, I came to believe I had some control over my attitude. For the rest of my life, I will occasionally find myself riding the wave of sadness, but with the knowledge that the wave will eventually return me to the safety of shore.

"Also, I came to understand the statement by violinist, Isaac Stern, that in America we need to understand that the arts are not a frill; they are not mere entertainment; they are an integral part of who we are. After our diagnosis, I started making jewelry, painting furniture, making shadow boxes, and gardening. One April day, when I was depressed about my son's addiction, I remembered T.S. Eliot's line, "…April is the cruelest month." Then I looked out my kitchen window at the sun-drenched grass, that lovely yellow-green that only spring can render, and the color green lifted me and carried me through the day. Observing nature up-close and immersing oneself in the imaginative-creative process can provide peace and joy and balm to a suffering soul.

"In addition, a sense of humor is important.

"Now, onto my next topic: you, who I am counting on.

"I met some of you at the genetics conference in Philadelphia last fall. After I introduced my family and said a few words, I was overwhelmed by the number of you who descended on me to say you had never met anyone with myotonic dystrophy. One was Dr. Tom Cooper at Baylor. Since then, he has spoken to over 200 patients in Southern California at the only active American support group organized solely for myotonic dystrophy families. Over lunch in Houston a few months before his talk, he asked what I thought he should say to this group. I said, you can give them hope; emphasize that there is a group of investigators spending a goodly portion of their lives in passionate pursuit of a treatment for this disease. They care about finding a treatment...Yes, there are people who care. At a very basic human level, that is what all of us yearn for.

"A treatment might not be developed in my lifetime but I can surely enjoy each day of the process in the meantime. Here in Kyoto, I am watching you work your alchemy with presentations and collaborations over conference tables and dinner. And the process of watching you work gives me hope, like looking at spring-green.

"I will now take the liberty of speaking for myself and all DM patients to express deep appreciation to you, Professor Oshawa, and all the Japanese organizers of the consortium, Professor Peter Harper, all of whom have contributed to the current understanding of the disease mechanism of myotonic dystrophy, the sponsors of the consortium, the AINO Aging Institute, the Association Francais contre les Myopathies, and the Muscular Dystrophy Association as well as my friends and family, who are not here tonight, but have supported the Hunter Research Fund.

"I want to express special appreciation to Dr. Ashizawa, or Tee, and the rest of the Baylor team. You have been willing to educate me in a whole new language of transgenic mice, Drosophila, CTG expansions, and SIX5. At Baylor, you endured the devastating flood in June; you lost laboratories, materials, and irretrievable research time. As the poet, Robert Burns, who never met a transgenic mouse, prophetically wrote, "The best laid schemes of mice and men [go oft awry], and leave us naught but grief and pain for promised joy." You lost your mice and experienced grief and pain, but you immediately re-laid your schemes, and with determination, perseverance, and dedication forged ahead.

"In the aftermath of the terrorist acts on September 11, Tee e-mailed me: "We try to save lives and prevent disability, spending hours [upon] hours, after years of training, to save one life in ICU. [Yesterday] thousands of lives were lost in seconds. I feel all kinds of emotions inside of me. Yet, we must proceed. Our goal and determination for DM research will not be shaken!" His words symbolize the kind of energy and synergy I feel among you, representing many nations of the free world.

"I am deeply grateful for all your efforts, even though I don't always understand them; you do, and that's what matters. I am banking on your unfettered passion, your extraordinary talents and expertise to find a treatment for DM. I will continue to cheer from the sidelines. Again, let me reiterate: I am a Most Happy and Honored Fellow to be with you this week."

They gave me a standing ovation.

Although I had not spoken publicly since high school, I persevered in spite of my usual nervousness and flushing. Drained but happy, I glided back to my room and slept exceedingly well.

Just before I had left Atlanta, the chairman of the consortium had e-mailed to ask if I would be willing to speak to a group of nursing students, along with Tee, at the conclusion of the meeting. I tailored another version of my talk for nurses. Tee would present the scientific information and I would share a family perspective. I assumed we would address a classroom of students. However, upon arriving in Kyoto the chairman told us that we would be addressing 400 students and faculty in a large auditorium. He showed me a poster advertising our talks like the ones posted on campus bulletin boards. Was I really up to the task? I wondered especially when he requested my curriculum vitae. Never having written a CV, I created one in long-hand on the tour bus to the Golden Pavilion the next afternoon.

At the close of the conference, Tee, the chairman, and I were whisked off to Osaka, an hour away, to meet with the psychiatrist, who was the primary sponsor of the IDMC and the owner of the hospital and nursing school. We were taken to his private dining room where the four of us were served lunch in Bento boxes filled with mysterious delicacies. Mimicking my lunch companions, I ate shrimp with the shells on while silently convincing myself I was partaking of an extra dose of calcium and fiber. Such a dish was not on any menu at the Gulf of Mexico restaurants I had frequented all my life.

We finished lunch and were escorted through a pedestrian tunnel that probably seemed longer than it was and entered an anteroom adjacent to the auditorium. Turning my head, I freshened my lipstick and pushed loose hair from my face. I cleared my throat and skimmed my notes one more time. As we approached the first row in the auditorium, I saw my newest best friend, Takako, and her husband in the audience. Takako beamed with her infectious smile and waved with rapidly bending fingers.

Finally, Tee was introduced. As the lights dimmed, he began his power point lecture on the science of myotonic dystrophy. An hour later, returning to his seat beside me, he whispered. "I put them all to sleep!—*Look!*"

Then it was my turn to speak while the Chairman translated my talk sentence by sentence into Japanese. I perspired under the hot stage lights, as my talk and the translation droned on endlessly. If I had not been standing, I would surely have fallen asleep myself. If I had anticipated this slow process, I would have made my talk much shorter.

After the perfunctory applause, Tee and I returned to the stage a second time and were each presented with an enormous bouquet of flowers. To my delight, there had been flowers, flowers *everywhere*—in the ante-room adjacent to the auditorium, on the lectern from which Tee spoke, and on the table, behind which I spoke. We were then whisked back to Kyoto in the psychiatrist's Rolls Royce and dined at the Chrysanthemum Restaurant. Once again, the Maiko girls from the banquet hovered around, pouring sake, and giggling. Tee was given a bottle of fine sake as a gift, and I received a beautiful, red, black, white, and gold fabric relief of a Maiko girl, hand-stitched and presented to me by the wife of the president of the hospital and nursing school. Peering into her expressive eyes, I yearned desperately to speak. But she knew not a word of English, and I knew no Japanese. I tried my best to show appreciation with exaggerated nods and smiles. Having done all sorts of sewing in my life, I marveled at her creation, designed and carefully executed by her very own hands, a gift of time and talent I will cherish forever.

14. Becoming a Patient Advocate

The morning after my speech at the IDMC-3 meeting, Dr. Harper approached me in his refreshingly humble, English way and said, "Very nice talk last night. I would like to ask you to consider being a reader for a little hundred-page book called *Myotonic Dystrophy, The Facts* that I have written for families living with myotonic dystrophy."

I nearly dropped my coffee. I could never have imagined having this opportunity. Here was the leading authority on DM asking me, a novice, to comment on his writings. But then I remembered, I had been an English major so I could at least make sure the book was structured properly and could critique his presentation of the facts as I knew them. I thanked him and accepted his request with some trepidation, but also a lot of joy. It was not long before I received the manuscript from Dr. Harper. I got to work and read it from cover to cover several times. I started making my red marks until I felt I had been a good reader and editor. I sent it off to Dr. Harper and within about a week received a thoughtful email thanking me for a job well done. He did, in his English way, point out that many of my red marks reflected an American's perception and critique of English writing style and word usage. Oh, I was so embarrassed. But it was my first time editing this kind of book, and I forgave myself for not being aware of the differences in use of words or structure.

Several weeks later, Tee asked me to join the planning committee for the next scientific meeting, IDMC-4, to be held at the University of Glasgow in April of 2003. I felt honored and eager to oblige.

During this time, I became glued to the internet trying to find everything I could about DM. Even more important, I began to seek out others who had the disease and to learn more about their experiences. I had extensive talks with the members of my family about their DM symptoms and how they adversely affected their lives and how they coped with their symptoms. I also began to search for others in Georgia and the South as well as other parts of the USA. In the process, I realized how challenging it was to identify people with DM. For the same reasons that it took so long to find out what was happening with Hunter, many people had never been diagnosed. And, because of the nature of the disease, many of those who knew they had DM did not have the motivation and energy to become active and to reach out. As a result, many were isolated and hard to find.

At this time, Dr. Harper was beginning another book to address these patient and family needs. Physicians and researchers attending a small international workshop sponsored by the European Neuromuscular Centre (ENMC) in The Netherlands in 2001, developed an idea for a book that would educate physicians and patients about myotonic dystrophy. It was to be titled, *Myo-*

tonic Dystrophy — Present Management, Future Therapy. It is now often referred to among affected families as the *Black Book*. Dr. Harper and a small committee outlined the topics to be included. One chapter was "Support Groups for Myotonic Dystrophy and Their Role: An American Family Perspective." I felt honored when Dr. Harper asked me to write this chapter, even though at the time I did not fully understand the importance of patient advocacy and support groups. After researching the topic, I was disheartened to discover only one active DM group in the entire country. It had been founded by Ed and Alice Gunderson in Southern California a few years before. Ed had DM and suffered greatly toward the end of his life. He was bed ridden, and often on a ventilator, for three years before his death. I also learned about the Myotonic Dystrophy Support Group in England that had been founded by Margaret Bowler in 1989. It was run by volunteers and dedicated to offering the hand of friendship and support to all those affected by DM.

When I arrived at the conference in Glasgow in 2003, I was awed to see the University of Glasgow for the first time, a 550-year old architectural gem with stone spires that majestically pierced the ever-changing Scottish sky. Conference attendees were greeted by the waving arms of blooming forsythia and their daffodil companions tottering in the wind. I no longer felt like a newcomer, as I had in Japan. Now I was an integral part of the conference. I had my legs and was running hard, looking for more to do and more people to meet. I was beginning to formulate how I was going to put my passion and experience to work.

On the final afternoon of the meeting, I was the lead-off speaker in front of 150 DM investigators from around the world and 150 members of Margaret Bowler's British Myotonic Dystrophy Support Group, all convened in the same lecture hall. The number of affected family members in attendance had increased dramatically from the Kyoto conference where I had been the lone patient participant.

In addition to presenting the different reactions to the disease within my immediate family, I pressed for more brain research, especially in the childhood-onset form of the disease. "The physical aspects of DM are difficult and often very cruel; but for our family, to date, the cognitive and behavioral aspects have been the most challenging." Also, I boldly suggested that DM be included in the Diagnostic and Statistical Manual for Mental Disorders (the DSM). But most important, being there with Margaret and her group from the UK, I knew that it was time to develop support groups in the U.S. I realized that I could not make the necessary impact by doing this work on my own.

Shortly after I returned home from the conference, I received a lengthy e-mail from Mario Pereira, a post doc at the University of Glasgow that affirmed the need for bringing patients and researchers together. I recalled his jitteriness during his very first presentation at the Hunter Fund brainstorming session in Philadelphia. Three years later in Glasgow, I had noticed how confident he had become as he presented his research paper, interacted with peers in a pub, and danced at a Kaleigh. His e-mail first described the success of the conference. And then he wrote:

> ...I must confess that there were a couple of times when I had
> tears in my eyes whilst listening to your touching story...you
> always manage to give us that extra motivation...listening to your

stories makes me acknowledge that DM is much more than a tissue culture flask or a DNA sample inside a test tube...makes me want to work much harder.

In 2005, a couple of years after the conference in Glasgow, I had the opportunity to present a patient's perspective on DM at an NIH-sponsored conference in Washington, "The Burden of Muscle Disease." This conference was mandated by the Muscular Dystrophy Care Act, a bill passed by Congress to increase funding for research in the muscular dystrophies. It wasn't until later that I realized that this conference was an effort to jump-start *translational research* for the muscular dystrophies. It had become clear to the NIH that a lot of promising medical research never made it beyond the lab. They wanted to start more effectively using research to improve healthcare outcomes. At this conference, I became more aware of the countless steps and millions of dollars required to move research to clinical trials and ultimately to apply the findings to new treatments or devices that would benefit the patient population.

Attending the conference were physicians, scientists, representatives from the NIH, Muscular Dystrophy Association (MDA), Federal Drug Administration (FDA), pharmaceutical companies, and health economists, as well as several patient advocates representing their own form of muscular dystrophy. One advocate was Pat Furlong, Founder and CEO of the Parent Project Muscular Dystrophy, a patient advocacy group representing Duchene Muscular Dystrophy, probably the most well-known form of MD and the focus of the Jerry Lewis telethon. Pat had organized this group of families, and it had become a major force in moving research forward to learn more about the disease that took the lives of both of her young sons.

The representatives from the FDA emphasized the importance of patient voice and participation at all phases of research. They noted that before the FDA would approve a clinical trial, they wanted to know what level of importance patients placed on that particular treatment. In order to conduct their research, investigators needed information and biopsies from patients to help in discovering the disease mechanism. Patients also play a key role in Congressional hearings and lobbying efforts to get funding for their particular diseases. Moreover, advocacy groups could expedite the research process by raising funds. These discussions confirmed that we had to have an advocacy group and encourage investigators to pursue grants available from the NIH. Other muscular dystrophies and many other diseases already had well organized patient groups, but myotonic dystrophy still did not. It was a seminal moment for me. I had been exchanging e-mails with many investigators. Dr. Tom Cooper underscored the importance of patient voices:

> ...I think it is important for you to know how much of an impact you have had on the research community in the field of myotonic dystrophy...in giving scientists a perspective they would not be privy to otherwise. It does have an impact on what questions we choose to address...For example, we have designed a mouse model that will allow us to work on issues of brain development...

Through the years, I have asked myself how the confusion among patients and doctors can be rectified.

First, DM should be re-classified as a *multisystemic disease*, an umbrella term under which neuromuscular, central nervous system, cardiac, gastrointestinal, and other symptoms logically fall. Dr. Krawiecki reminded me recently that it was Hunter's learning and behavioral issues, not muscle weakness that prompted us to make our first appointment with him.

Second, practitioners can learn about the broad range of symptoms from patients themselves. Story-telling and concrete examples are stellar teaching methods. In 2007, Dr. Hopkins at Emory School of Medicine invited Dr. Krawiecki and me to assist in introducing the neuromuscular diseases to first year medical students. Dr. Hopkins was the attending physician for the neurology fellows who administered the EMG to Hunter, Larry, and me in 1989—the ones who shrugged in dismay when my test results were negative. Dr. Hopkins asked Dr. Krawiecki and me—after a scientific and medical description of the various muscle diseases with an emphasis on DM—to re-enact our first appointment where he tentatively diagnosed Hunter with the hand-grip test; after the skit, I told our family story. In August of 2011, we made our sixth annual presentation to the freshman class. In 2012, Larry joined Dr. Krawiecki and me in the reenactment. Emory also recorded the reenactment and my presentation. I'm happy to say that, by now, over eight hundred medical school students at Emory have been introduced to this rare disease. The recording will enable many more to learn about the complexities of DM and the challenges in diagnosing it.

Third, families can become effective advocates and supporters for research, education, and the development of treatments. A family in Virginia had two young children who were diagnosed with the congenital form of DM. In their need to *do something,* they discovered an investigator in myotonic dystrophy at the University of Virginia, right at their back door. And that is where they have focused their energy to raise money to support research and to educate medical providers.

There are countless other stories of patient advocacy efforts that have helped patients and their families to cope and to advance research. The potential impact of these efforts came into sharper focus when I attended an annual conference of the Genetic Alliance in 2008, a nonprofit health advocacy organization committed to engaging individuals, families, and communities in transforming healthcare. Its network includes more than 1,200 disease-specific advocacy organizations, as well as thousands of universities, private companies, government agencies, and public policy organizations.

From talking with members of these groups, I learned that there is no formula for how best to advocate for a specific disease. Within each disease, there are different needs in the area of education for families and doctors, support, advocacy, and research. Across all groups, many people affected by a disease *feel an overwhelming need to do something to make a difference,* but individuals must forge their own paths that fit their talents, abilities, passion, persistence, and, most importantly, their need to feel better. In the act of giving, they are often blind-sided with unexpected rewards of a life of joy and connection that are much greater than they ever imagined.

While attending these conferences and writing the chapter for Dr. Harper on support groups, I felt an undercurrent of sadness as I realized how little support was available for families living with DM and facing the prospect that it will get worse with age and in successive generations. I recalled how I had felt so alone and hopeless those first few years. Yet, it wasn't until I spoke at the Burden of Muscle Disease Conference in 2005 that I truly understood the importance of establishing a voice and a face for this perplexing disease and working hand-in-hand with the research community to de-mystify the disease and develop viable treatments. I talked to Tee about the lack of DM support, advocacy, and fundraising groups. He encouraged me to become the voice of DM in the USA by bringing together patients and caregivers to provide information and support for families dealing with the complexities of DM.

As a testament to the increasing recognition of the importance of patient voices, the organizer for the IDMC-5 biennial meeting in Quebec in 2005 asked me to invite 25 affected American family members to the meeting. In addition, he asked permission for the Hunter Fund to pay their travel expenses. Tee and I agreed. He contacted some and I reached out to the others. I informed each of the invitees of my intention to spearhead the founding of a national DM patient organization at the meeting in Quebec.

During the meeting, I hosted a buffet dinner for more than thirty people—including six American physicians. I created an agenda and led the discussion about founding a national patient support and advocacy group. Jeremy Kelley, John Brekka, and Barry Wald who were attending the Quebec meeting stepped forward to help. We agreed to push forward with the organization. It was so exciting to have others working with me to move the organization forward. It was not long before the Myotonic Dystrophy Foundation (MDF), a 501(c)(3) non-profit organization was formed.

This organization focuses primarily on education, advocacy, and research. A critical part of the internet presence is designed for family members to communicate with others to learn more about our disease and to get emotional support and practical advice. Happily, many people are finding answers to disease-related questions; but perhaps equally important, they are no longer traveling this path alone. In addition to connecting families with each other, the site interfaces with the investigative research community, providing education for patients and medical professionals and financially supporting research.

We were not alone in these initiatives. In November of 2006, the Myotonic Dystrophy Toronto support group was established to connect DM families in the Greater Toronto and surrounding areas of Southern Ontario to share information, resources, and mutual support. In 2010, the scope of the support group broadened from regional to national and the name was changed to Myotonic Dystrophy Canada.

I served as Chair of the Board of the MDF for the first four years. With my colleagues from Florida to California, we started by having weekly conference calls. There was no lack of ideas that needed to be implemented. We hired Lisa Harvey, who has an affected child, as executive director. We rented some office space, brought on new board members, and developed a website. It was a very exciting time in my life as I, along with a handful of dedicated board members, strove to create a national force. While all the organization of the MDF was happening, I continued to maintain and expand my relationship with the clinicians and researchers. It was a very busy time.

Over time, I finally admitted and realized that I did not find my highest calling was to manage the details of a board spread over a wide geographical area with conference calls and emails. Therefore, in 2009, I stepped down as chair. I felt that I had done what I was meant to do and others could continue the good work of the growing and thriving MDF. I knew that I was the primary connection between patients and the research community and acknowledged that was where my skills and passion lay. Involvement in the DM investigative community had become a vital part of my life. My ideas and experiences were making significant contributions to research so I continued harnessing my curiosity and determination to learning more, developing mutual and collaborative relationships with investigators, and communicating my observations to them. Traveling this path and getting feedback from investigators, physicians, and patients continued to provide validation. It evolved into a balm that was not only soothing but also invigorating.

15. Reflections on Depression and Hope

Looking back on the last three decades, I now remember how paralyzed I felt after the diagnosis of myotonic dystrophy in my family. I was unable to raise myself off the couch and had the feeling I could do nothing to cure my children or myself. For the first time, I experienced deep depression. However, whether it was a mother's instinct or the inquisitiveness of my father, I still held onto the notion that there was hope. With a rekindled spirit, I rose off that sofa one day and dedicated my life to taking care of my children and seeking answers on how this disease was affecting them.

After a few years of trying to make sense out of multiple symptoms of my children as they appeared, and coming to grips with the reality of the disease, I set out to find a way to help support researchers in this field. I held onto the notion that therein lay the hope for clarifying the confusion about our disease and eventually developing a treatment. I did not initially strike out on a charted course with clear end-points in mind. At first, each effort was an entity unto itself: bringing my family together, fundraising, and speaking at an international conference of scientists and physicians. I completed each task and generally felt good about my involvement, only to find that another opportunity would arise. Ultimately, the fog lifted, the path became clear, and I realized I was truly on a journey. What began with concerns about my son's drool from his lower lip and the reading difficulties of both my children became my life's work. I embarked on a path to put a face on this complex disease, to bring understanding to those experiencing it, and to provide as much insight to the research community that might aid in the pursuit of a treatment.

At the core of it all lay an abiding and, as close-as-humanly possible, unconditional love for my children. It was painful to watch one child being teased and bullied by the outside world and the other acting out feelings of incompetence and stupidity. Although they perceived their worlds quite differently, neither one lived up to other people's expectations. The path I chose on behalf of my children is not unusual. Through the ages, parents, out of their deep love for their children, have sacrificed in order to enhance their chances of ultimately leading healthy, independent, productive lives.

As I walked this road, I learned that we can allow ourselves to go *through* the pain of facing and accepting our reality. We can give ourselves permission to feel depressed and angry and find a way to tell our story to release the angst.

As we ride the wave of sadness from time to time, we may find ourselves being dragged back across the line in the sand to confront once again the world's expectations of our children and ourselves. We may be overwhelmed with feelings of anger, fear, frustration, and indignation about a situation over which we have no control. In time, we can choose to force our way out of this place back into the realm of acceptance of our reality where we can nurture ourselves and others.

I have learned a lot from other people's stories, especially *Man's Search for Meaning* by Viktor Frankl. Interestingly, Ashby recommended this book to me because it was assigned for his high school psychology class. Although he probably did not read much of it, he did recognize the gist of the message and was spot on when he handed it to me saying: "Mom, here, this is your kind of book." After spending years in a concentration camp and observing many prisoners, Frankl learned that *one of man's primary motivational forces is one's freedom to transcend suffering and find meaning in life*, regardless of the circumstances. He observed that prisoners who managed to survive the horror of the camps shared some common characteristics, several of which I mentioned in my speech in Kyoto: sense of humor (even if grim or ironic humor) to help them rise above their situation if only for a few seconds; curiosity; belief in a higher power; belief that love is the ultimate and the highest goal to which man can aspire; artistic creation and expression, which was incorporated into their daily lives as often as possible in the form of cabarets where they shared songs, poems, and jokes; belief they had some control over their attitude; and recognition that it does not really matter what we expect from life, but rather what life expects from us in taking the responsibility to find the right answer to its problems.

As I read his book for the first time, I found myself cheering,

"Yes!" Initially I had perceived our diagnosis as a life sentence. Yet over the years, I had learned as Frankl states:

> "When facing a fate that cannot be changed, what then matters is to harness our unique, human potential at its best, which is to transform a personal tragedy into a triumph, to turn one's predicament into a human achievement. When we are no longer able to change a situation—just think of an incurable disease such as inoperable cancer [and, here, I add myotonic dystrophy] we are challenged to change ourselves." (Frankl, 1984/1992, p. 116).

We patients and family members sometimes find ourselves in such deep, emotional pain that we will do anything to extricate ourselves. We eventually reach a point—a tipping point—wherein lies a choice: to remain where we are or choose to galvanize ourselves and do something meaningful, something that feels good and starts us on an outward journey.

Over a period of years, I have come to believe that disease does not have to consume a life; it is but part of the overall pattern of our lives. In order to live fully, we must view life in its entirety. Different people affected by the same untreatable disease cope with it in vastly different ways, as I observe in my own family: Hunter, blessed with the gift of *anosognosia*, accepts it without question and anxiety; it is plain and simply a part of who he is. For Ashby, myotonic dystrophy enshrouds his entire life that, I venture to say, he hardly deems worth living. Larry, whose life has been profoundly influenced by DM, still attacks life with boundless energy and passion. He was born to take ideas and push them to fruition and his enthusiasm for my work, and confidence in my abilities, inspired and heartened me at every step on this path. And although I would not wish disease on anyone, and in spite of it nearly having snuffed me out, I have grown stronger because of it.

When we finally are able to reach outside of ourselves, to advocate and help others, a feeling of empowerment and strength germinates and grows. Acceptance and joy enable us to provide comfort and strength to those around us as the following story about Takako, the beautiful, young Japanese woman with whom I had the privilege of spending four days at the Kyoto conference in 2001, whose husband was an endocrinologist and a rising star in his field.

Late one November day in 2010, I returned home to discover a voice-mail from Takako. A sad, plaintive voice had replaced the upbeat tone I remembered. Beginning to cry, she hung up without conveying her reason for calling or leaving her phone number. I e-mailed her; but the message bounced back; as it did on my second try. I found her husband's e-mail address and sent him a message. I waited. Still no response. Months later, I received an e-mail from Takako:

> Dearest Shannon,
> It has been so long I saw you last.
> I've many thing to tell you. But, hard to tell…
> What do I need to tell you is about my husband.
> He had a car accident last November.
> He was on the way back from the hospital.
> Someone who's driving car.
> He crash my husband car…

Be know he was drinker...
If you don't mind.
May I going to see you?
Love,
Takako

Over the next couple of months, we exchanged e-mails and decided to meet in Los Angeles the following September. When we saw each other, it was a joyous reunion in spite of the rough times we had both been having. It was two human beings from different parts of the world supporting each other in our own cultural ways. We also acted like typical tourists as we walked Rodeo Drive, rode bikes to Venice Beach, and bought outlandish sunglasses in Hollywood.

The first night at dinner, over a glass of wine, Takako straightened herself, looked me squarely in the eye and said, "I know why I want to come and see you—I know why, 'cause I love to going to see someone who's know him, and 'cause I know you have many troubles with your sons. I know 'cause you told us in Japan. But—you seem happy. What I want to know: how can you have so many troubles and also be happy?"

I assured her that I was not always happy. I told her about my initial depression, five years in a therapy group...exercising... riding the wave. Everything. I told her about finally arriving at a point where I realized I had the ability to make choices about my attitude toward situations I encountered.

Takako paused. As she spoke, tears welled up in her dark eyes in the dimly-lit restaurant. "You the only one—the only one—who say, 'You, Takako, have your dreams taken away.'

Everyone else say, 'Poor Akiyoshi, he had such good dreams for his life. And now, he cannot have them."

After dinner the next night, Takako carefully placed three pastel sweetener packets on the table. They represented the cars involved in her husband's accident. She slowly moved them in the flickering candlelight while she explained step by step how the fatal accident had occurred. She desperately needed to tell her story.

Several days later, we returned to our respective homes. A week later, Takako sent me an e-mail to inform me that she was now sewing kids' wear for a school bazaar near her house. After a few weeks, she asked if I would please send her some yellow *Live Strong* bracelets that she also wanted to sell at the school event. She requested at least one small one for herself. "The bazaar is good fun," she wrote. "…I am happy to doing that. This is most good things, right?"

Months later I opened another e-mail from her:

Dearest Shannon,
I feel like, I am OK! Sometimes makes me sad because of my
husband
But, I can handle it.
Don't forget! Shannon You helping…
Love,
Takako

Time flowed in its inimitable way while e-mails passed between us. One day I received the following message:

Dearest Shannon,

...It was special time for me.

Won't be forgot what I done with you.

You have a special power...

Thank you again for everything from deeply in my heart...

Now I am able to think. Even I could know his life is short, I wished to be his wife.

Now, I am not sadness widow.

I am most happiness woman...

Shannon! Thank you!

Love,

Takako

If we do not choose to make that first move, how will we ever know what unique, hidden strengths we may have, what contributions we can make, what lives we may touch in unexpected ways, and how good we may feel taking action and living large in spite of our disease? Although many of us have been blindsided by the disease, we also have been blindsided by totally unexpected rewards when we have become advocates and activists.

Through my years of self-doubt, equivocation, self-confidence, fear, anger, joy, desperation, anxiety, calm, depression, and contentment, somehow, almost magically, persistence has always prevailed. Even when I got derailed and found myself sprawled on the ground, I always managed to get up and move forward again. Persistence is the connective stitching between the irregular shapes, varied sizes, textures, and colors of my life. The first day I turned to my art supplies when I was deeply depressed, I found a set of fabric pieces that I had carefully cut to make a quilt in the predictable, consistent log-cabin pattern. I long ago threw them away and now realize that for all these years I have been busy making a *crazy quilt*, every shape and texture different from the next, some pointed and jagged, some rounded and smooth, some beautifully embroidered; some as rough as a hair shirt, and others soft and shiny. It is comprised of solid colors and prints, checks and stripes; all the colors of the rainbow. It is not yet finished; one end is still jagged, awaiting the next swatch of my life to be added.

The Last Chapter

BY LARRY LORD, 2016

In late November of 2012, Shannon had her annual physical and gynecological exam. All reports indicated she had no negative health issues at all. She told both of her doctors that she was trying to lose some weight but otherwise agreed that she felt great. One encouraged her to "cut down on the carbs" and do more exercise but keep going as she had been. "You are doing great," they both said. She came home exuberant and looking forward to continuing her life as an activist.

The next week, she was walking with Esther Stokes, her "Friday walking friend" on their favorite path through neighborhoods, and along Peachtree Creek and Bobby Jones Golf Course. Along the way, they often stopped at the clubhouse at the golf course for a bathroom break. That day, she noticed that she had a stronger urge to get there but assumed it was just a matter of getting a little older.

A couple of weeks later, she was walking over a cobblestone

drive, lost her balance and tumbled to the ground. Although she had a scraped wrist and a mildly sore hip, her pride suffered most. She had always had great balance, so this fall was a surprise.

In contrast to Shannon, I have always considered myself "gyroscopically challenged." We often laughed at my nervousness whenever I saw Shannon in a precarious situation. We knew that my poor balance was not contagious and found this incident perplexing. Shannon pondered what was changing.

On Friday, January 11th, 2013, Shannon noticed some spotting. It bothered her enough to call John Drummond, our primary physician, and inform him of her concern. His thought that it was possibly a bladder infection. He prescribed antibiotics. But to be sure, he asked her to schedule an appointment with Barbara Croft, her gynecologist. She responded that she had just had her annual physicals, but John insisted she go see Barbara.

First thing Monday, she called for the appointment. Barbara was almost always fully booked months in advance but through Shannon's persistence, she got the appointment for right after lunch that same day. She and I arrived at Barbara's office well ahead of time. While we sat in the waiting room, Shannon recalled a few unusual physical symptoms she had noticed during the previous few weeks. As she shared these impressions with me, we began to feel nervous. Shannon was finally called back to the exam room. Barbara asked a few questions, gave her a quick pelvic exam and then told her to return on Wednesday for some precautionary biopsies. Barbara did not sound alarmed but … "biopsies" … that was not a comforting prospect.

On Wednesday, we arrived early. We waited. By now Shannon was truly apprehensive. She told me she was not looking forward to the biopsies. She recalled the experience of the removal of pieces of her body as extraordinarily painful. Barbara gave her pain medication and she successfully withstood the procedure. When we got home she went straight to bed. By this time, I had become nervous as well.

The conversation about what we might expect consumed the rest of the week and through the weekend. Monday was Martin Luther King Jr's birthday holiday, so we had to endure one more day of not knowing.

Tuesday morning, the phone rang early. It was Barbara. She got right to the point. "Shannon, the tests just came back. You have endometrial cancer." My heart sank as I watched and over-heard Shannon's side of the phone conversation and realized that the news was not good. Shannon hung up and immediately said, "I have cancer, the worst, most aggressive kind." We hugged and cried over this ominous news and the uncertainty that lay ahead. We talked for hours about: What does this mean? … What should we do next? … Can she be cured? Who among the doctors involved with myotonic dystrophy should we call? What would the oncologist say?

Barbara recommended Dr. Burrell, an oncologist with whom she worked and had come to respect. Shannon called for an ap-pointment, and fortunately Dr. Burrell agreed to see her the fol-lowing morning. We arrived well before the scheduled appoint-ment. The exam did not take long. When she returned, we were ushered to a special consultation room. After what seemed like a very long time, Dr. Burrell came in, sat down, and reiterated what Barbara had told Shannon. "You have a very aggressive type of tumor. It is called MMMT, malignant mixed Mullerian tumor. You need to have surgery as soon as possible." He told his assistant to arrange for a CT scan right away and to schedule the surgery. As we drove home, Shannon and I realized we were both apprehensive of what lay ahead. If fact, we were downright scared.

The assistant had been able to schedule the appointment the next morning. Shannon and I got off early. She was concerned about the CT scan because during a previous scan, she had become ill after drinking the barium sulfate which was needed to enhance the clarity. When the medical technician learned that Shannon was allergic to the barium sulfate, he said they would not do the scan until the oncologist confirmed that it would be okay. The doctor was not available so we had to leave without the scan.

Dr. Burrell's assistant called to tell us that the doctor had determined that Shannon could proceed without drinking the barium sulfate. She told us to come back on Friday, the earliest time they could reschedule. Friday was slow in coming. We got little sleep discussing what was next.

We arrived for the scan early. Shannon was taken back for the scan as soon as we got there. She was required to lie on the table without moving. She knew it was important to get a clear picture, but, lying there for two hours was excruciatingly painful.

We returned home to find a message from the oncologist's assistant saying they had an opening for surgery three weeks hence.

"Three weeks?" I shouted. "And, this is the most aggressive type of tumor!" I immediately decided I would find another doctor who would hopefully respond more quickly to the urgency of the situation. As it turns out, our long-time neighbor, Disja, stopped by for a visit. After listening to our concern, she suggested that we see Ben Benigno, an oncologist and close friend. She called Ben's private cell phone and, briefly explained Shannon's situation. She handed the phone to me.

After a brief conversation, Ben told me he would see Shannon Monday morning and, could foresee doing the surgery later in the week, two weeks ahead of the other surgeon. He said his nurse would tell us that he was fully booked but to inform her that Dr. Benigno had said to schedule an appointment anyway. He also told me to have all the records from the gynecologist and the other oncologist sent to his office as soon as possible.

Shannon and I arrived at Dr. Benigno's office Monday morning. We waited in a finely decorated waiting room with attractive and comfortable furniture accented by original paintings by Dr. Benigno's wife, Sheila. We were soon escorted into Dr. Benigno's personal office and were offered a seat on a comfortable sofa. Dr. Benigno arrived and pulled his chair close to the sofa. He showed genuine compassion, giving us his undivided attention. Shannon would later tell others that his bedside manner made her feel that she was his only patient.

He said he had read the medical notes from the gynecologist and would read the oncologist's records as soon as they arrived. But, even though he said he already understood the severity of the situation, he wanted Shannon to have another CT scan. We told him that she had already had the scan, but he wanted to have his radiologist do her own and read it herself. Based on these early reports, he was going to schedule surgery for Thursday. It would include doing a complete hysterectomy along with the removal of the omentum and appendix. He instructed us to return on Wednesday after he had reviewed the results of the new CT scan.

Even though she was totally consumed by this news, Shannon went into her typical "teaching" mode and began to inform Dr. Benigno about the dangers of anesthesia on myotonic dystrophy patients, especially any medication with muscle relaxers. He was at least curious, listened closely, and said he would arrange for a special pre-op conference with the anesthesiologist.

We were then escorted to the CT scan. Shannon hesitated before she drank the barium sulfate but did not argue about getting ill since she realized that the more the doctors knew, the better the chances of success from the surgery. Fortunately, the procedure took only about ten minutes, a stark difference from the previous one. Also, she did not get sick.

After reading the results of the CT scan, Dr. Benigno reported that it was generally consistent with the earlier information, but he now had a clearer picture of the location of two tumors that needed to be removed. He scheduled surgery for 7:30 the next morning and said that Shannon was to check into the hospital about 6:00 a.m. At that point, Shannon was totally exhausted and the thought of going home and getting up at 5:00 a.m. to return to the hospital was overwhelming. The nurse who was handling all the details for the surgery observed Shannon's stress. She realized that going home and returning the next morning was not a good idea. The kind nurse had Dr. Benigno write the orders for Shannon to be admitted to the hospital right away.

I got the car, picked her up at the front door of the doctor's office, and drove her around to the hospital entrance. I parked in a parking deck that seemed correct, but it turned out to be a long way from the hospital registration. There were no wheelchairs in sight, so Shannon with her mounting fatigue, struggled to walk the whole distance. We arrived in the waiting room to register and were faced with a process that seemed to take an eternity. The paperwork was mountainous. Even with Shannon clearly in poor shape, they did not speed up the process. I filled out most of the paperwork while Shannon was dealing with the uncertainty of our future. I tried to say something encouraging, but she quickly pointed out there was nothing optimistic about what was about to happen.

Shannon was finally admitted and taken to her room for the night. After perfunctorily checking vital signs and asking routine questions, the nurse's aide returned with a bowel-clearing stimulant. As I recalled from my last colonoscopy, it requires drinking one 8 oz. glass every 10 to 15 minutes until the bottle is empty, which is about a gallon of liquid. Shannon asked why she was having to take that horrible stuff. The aide did not know, but said she would find out.

In about an hour, the first reaction to the stimulant took effect. It came quickly, and Shannon made quite a mess in the bed since she had not been told to be prepared to rush to the toilet. She pushed the call button, while I ran out to find a nurse. The nurse's aide arrived and to her displeasure realized her next task. I could not believe it, but she was actually irate that Shannon had not gotten to the toilet in time. She told me to wait in the hall. After getting Shannon to the toilet and helping her get cleaned up, the nurse's aide began working on the bed clean up. After I was allowed back in the room and Shannon in a clean bed, she told me that, although there was nothing amusing about the situation, she did briefly smile when the disagreeable aide had to clean up the mess.

We did learn later that the reason for bowel cleansing was to clear the colon of any fecal residue because the tumor might be attached to the colon. If that was the case, then that section of the colon would have to be removed. We were beginning to understand that the extent of her cancer would not be known until after the surgery and further biopsies and scans. Shannon admitted this did not look good at all.

Trying to stay positive, I asked her to wait until we knew more and please try not to worry. She told me that from what she had learned about MMMT and felt in her soul, it was likely a one-way trip. I could not believe that my Shannon, always strong and confident, was bordering on the fatalistic. I continued to encourage her with every ounce of love as much as I could convey.

Shannon had me ask Tee (Dr. Ashizawa) if harvesting body parts removed during surgery would be beneficial for DM research. He said, "Absolutely," and told us he would send information about the procedures for harvesting, refrigerating, or freezing, packing, and shipping tissues. I was relieved to have something tangible on which I could focus. I got right to work making sure everything was organized.

At 6:30 am the next morning, Shannon awoke as I sat beside her on the bed. She was always thinking about her myotonic dystrophy and reminded me that we had to talk with the anesthesiologist. That seemed to be all she wanted. I squeezed her hand and said I would make sure the anesthesiologist understood. I had put together a loose-leaf binder, including the anesthesia guidelines that Shannon had pushed to have developed and published by the MDF. The guidelines strongly suggested that postoperative pain control should be managed without the use of opioids or benzodiazepines since they were known to result in respiratory depression and aspiration. If they were used, she had to be carefully monitored.

My worries about the consequences of using the wrong anesthesia momentarily masked my deep concern for Shannon's well-being and the seriousness of what was beyond the surgery. But her mind was going in a different direction. As she was rolled to the pre-op room, she talked to me about the boys and her concern for their future. I listened intently but mostly thought and spoke about her well-being, not the boys, although I did realize that I would be responsible for them until she recovered.

The lead anesthesiologist came to the pre-op area and paid close attention as we explained the ramifications of incorrect anesthesiology with a myotonic dystrophy patient. He had read the guidelines and asked intelligent questions, and, unlike our previous encounters with doctors, there was no sarcasm. In fact, he assured us that Shannon would be safe and the anesthesia would not have any negative impact on her during surgery. At least that was one thing Shannon and I did not have to worry about at this point.

At the appointed hour, the surgical staff came to roll her to the OR. I kissed her on the forehead, looked her in the eyes. told her I loved her and would be there when she awoke. She admitted later that it was a level of sincerity she had not seen for a long time.

All during the very long morning, I called family and friends to give updates. At one point, the pathology technician came to tell me he was packing Shannon's removed tissues and wanted me to see how carefully he had done his job in accordance with the instructions from Tee. He let me know that he would personally be labeling the boxes for FedEx to pick up and deliver.

About three hours later, Dr. Benigno came to the waiting room to tell me Shannon was in recovery. He said that the operation went well and he thought they had gotten everything.

It was early afternoon when Shannon awakened from her anesthesia-induced sleep. She began to moan almost immediately with worse pain than she had ever experienced. The nurse explained to me the lighter anesthesia recommend by the guidelines was just not accomplishing what was needed to recover from the surgery. It was important to have sufficient pain medication to rest and recuperate. I called Tee who agreed that morphine was critical to recovery. I don't know if Shannon agreed or not, but the morphine brought great relief and sleep with the hope of healing. (As she told people later, "the morphine did not kill me.")

When stabilized, she was moved to her room. Over the next few days, the nursing staff cared for Shannon in a most supportive way. They soon ordered Shannon out of bed for walks around the corridor. Even with the exercise, her GI functions were slow in getting back to normal. As a result, bile was building up in her stomach, causing her to vomit. About the fourth day, they did an X-ray to see if there was any blockage but none had developed. The GI doctor ordered a placement of a tube through Shannon's nose into her stomach to drain the bile. It was irritatingly uncomfortable. She became agitated, trying to pull the tube out. She was given medication to calm her down. When I arrived early the next morning I found her in a deep sleep. I could not get any response.

I went to the nurse to find out what was going on and learned that someone ordered Ativan, a benzodiazepine, one that was prohibited by the guidelines. It was a frustrating reminder that, even with our best efforts to inform the medical staff about DM, the tendency to follow the usual procedures and medication regimens overrode this critical information. It was late that day before Shannon could communicate, stay awake, and walk down the hall. The good news was that, upon waking, she realized her GI track had begun to work and she would not have to continue with the tube.

Despite the discomfort, Shannon had many moments of joy as friends came to visit on a frequent basis. I was buoyed up as I saw her with her close friends Esther, Renie, Charmian, Arlene, Ada, Barbara, and Linton, sharing deeply felt support and love. I kept in touch with Shannon's family quite often by phone. Her sister Katie and her brother-in-law Donny drove up from Mobile to be with Shannon as well as to help me with the parental and household responsibilities. Friends delivered casseroles and other food to the house. Linton, whose son runs a famous restaurant bakery in Atlanta, would bring loaves of bread that had not been sold by late afternoon and put them in our mailbox. Arlene helped with Hunter's transportation. The list of support and loving friendship goes on.

Finally, after ten days, Dr. Benigno said it was time that Shannon be allowed to go home. He informed us that he would start chemotherapy the end of the week. The next day, we packed up and journeyed home. As usual, Shannon, even in these difficult circumstances, had created personal connections and a sense of community. Before we left, she said goodbye to all the nurses and many of the other patients on the floor. Being home really boosted Shannon's spirit. However, she began to focus on her concern about the chemotherapy.

I engaged a sitter service that provided certified nurse's assistants to be with Shannon as soon as she returned home. Initially we had 24-hour support but later eliminated the night help since I had learned I could support Shannon, and she preferred that. One of the sitters became Shannon's friend. Shannon would sit in the bed, the sitter in the chair by the bed, and they would talk for hours. I felt, with all the support from her friends, her sister Katie, and the sitter service, I could spend a little time attending to some of my business affairs.

Shannon began to get stronger, was able to walk around the house, and join the family for meals. Then came the chemotherapy. We learned that she had to go in the day before her first infusion to have her vital signs and weight documented to ensure that the mixture of chemotherapy drugs was appropriate for her current condition. The next day we made the trip back to the infusion center so she could begin her series of therapy. It was a daunting moment when she was hooked up and the drip began. The infusion went better than expected. We returned home, and for the next day and a half she was in great spirits. The steroids that are part of the regimen seemed to do their magic. But when the steroids wore off, she felt terrible. Gradually her strength returned, but by then it was time for the next infusion. She had an infusion every other week; the same cycle of feeling okay, then terrible, then better, was the pattern.

After Shannon had been taking chemotherapy treatments, I sent this email to family and friends to provide an overview and update on Shannon's condition:

Shannon had her surgery on January 31st which consisted of a complete hysterectomy plus removal of her appendix and omentum. She was in the ICU for the first 36 hours. I carried around the anesthesia guidelines so everyone knew the rules. We did have to break protocol and use morphine due to the intense pain she was experiencing, but she was on telemetry all the time. While on oxygen she had constant attention by the respiratory tech. There were many episodes of atrial fibrillation, especially when the pain was intense, so she was put on small doses of Sotalol. I was on the phone a number of times with Dr. Bill Groh and Dr. Bobby Smith, her local cardiologists. She returned home February 9th and steadily gained strength to be ready for chemotherapy which began on February 22nd. She was fine the next couple of days then the chemo drugs hit her. Today she is feeling better. Her current drugs are Taxol and Carboplatin to be administered over the next 18 weeks.

After the first six weeks, it was time to have another CT scan so the doctors could observe what was happening, good or bad. A couple of days after the scan, we arrived for our appointment, anxious to learn the results. Holding hands in the peaceful waiting room, we were called to see the doctor. But instead of going to Dr. Benigno's office, we were soon escorted to a small conference room. That immediately raised our fears. Shannon and I realized we were about to hear unwelcomed news. Dr. Benigno entered and immediately said that after the CT scan had been read by the radiologist, they discovered the tumors were back and growing. He said that he was going to change the chemotherapy to a more aggressive combination and told us Shannon was scheduled for the next infusion that Friday. We left the doctor's office with few words spoken and no thoughts of joy, only the devastating news reverberating into our heads.

The doctor ordered a stent to be put in Shannon's urethra so that, as the tumors grew, her ability to urinate would not be restricted. When we visited the urologist for a pre-op consultation, the receptionist asked for the radiological report. I had not been given a copy, so the assistant called and had it faxed. When it arrived, I asked for a copy and read the report. To my horror, I learned that one of the original tumors had increased by several centimeters and that new ones had appeared. I realized with dismay the doctor had not "gotten everything" as he had hoped. In fact, some of the original tumors were still there and growing.

By this time, Shannon began to think about her friends who had previously dealt with cancer. For many of them, their cancer had gone into remission after surgery, chemotherapy, or radiation, and they were still living happy and productive lives years later. But some of them had suffered greatly as a result of one or more of those procedures and their outcomes were not as positive. Shannon made it clear to me that she was determined to die with dignity and would not let heroic acts prolong her life.

We arrived for the infusion, we found the hospital psychologist and a social worker waiting for us. They had learned from the nurse who had given her a checkup the day before that Shannon was debating whether to proceed with the next round of chemotherapy. As I sat there listening, I was thankful for the compassionate way they interacted with Shannon. The conversation was deep and introspective as Shannon struggled to come to grips with whether continuing chemotherapy was the best course to take. After more than two hours of this counseling session, Shannon told them that for the sake of Hunter, Ashby, and me, she would proceed with the treatment to see if it made any change. I wept as the counselors left. When I hugged Shannon, she kept her gaze out the window and said nothing. The chemotherapy was administered.

Following the infusion, Shannon had a pain in her abdomen. We visited Dr. Amber Degryse, a pulmonologist, and learned that there was a buildup of fluid in her pleural cavity which required a thoracentesis, a procedure to remove the fluid. The fluid buildup continued, so after the second thoracentesis, Dr. Degryse told us that a catheter needed to be implanted to drain the pleural cavity on a regular basis. We were dismayed at the prospect that the fluid would continue to build up and that of yet another surgical procedure.

As I was leaving her office, Dr. Degryse, put her hand on my shoulder and said, "Bless you."

To prepare for the surgery, Dr. Degryse prescribed antibiotics to ward off possible infection. But soon after she was on the antibiotic, Shannon began to experience atrial fibrillation as a result of the chosen antibiotic. As atrial fibrillation became more pronounced, I took Shannon to the emergency room. The ER staff admitted her to the hospital and took her off the antibiotics. Dr. Benigno came by the room to discuss more about her condition. He agreed that continuing the antibiotic was not good and suggested that it would be best to postpone the next round of chemotherapy until the heart condition was normalized. However, after reviewing new test results, he changed his mind, "I will keep you in the hospital until Friday", which was two days hence. "We can do the infusion here in the hospital bed."

Shannon cleared her throat and stated emphatically, "That's it. I am not going to continue with chemotherapy. We all know that it is not working. I would like to talk with the people in palliative care."

My heart sank. I had feared this day would come. With Shannon's brave decision, it was time to move in a new direction.

Shannon asked Dr. Benigno who he might recommend for end of life care providers. He recommended Crossroads Hospice since their two practices often worked together. Shannon said, "Please have someone from Crossroads come and meet with us."

After Dr. Benigno left, Shannon said to me, "We all know this is futile. I am ready to approach death with dignity. I just want to be close to you, the boys, and my friends and family for the days I have left."

A representative from Crossroads knocked on the hospital door and, in a rather matter of fact way, confirmed Shannon's commitment, reviewed the services they provided, and prepared the paperwork for Shannon to sign. Shannon had no hesitation.

When we arrived back home from the hospital, the representative from Crossroads was there to meet us. She was very organized. She gave me instructions about medications, reactions to certain problems that would definitely arise, and told me what to do when her final moments come.

The tough thing was notifying the family of Shannon's decision. I had kept them up to date by phone for close friends and family, and by email to her wide circle of friends. On May 8th, I sent my next to last notification:

> The therapies to stave off Shannon's cancer have not been effective. So, on Friday, we began the next leg of Shannon's journey with palliative care at home. The hospice team is helping us respond to the physical pain and identifiable symptoms but also to our emotional apprehension and anxiety.
>
> We have learned that this is a journey with family and friends. To that end, I cannot say enough about the love and support we are receiving.
>
> Pray for the peace that passes all understanding as we grieve and process this, each in our own way. Let us pray that Shannon's strong voice, wisdom, curiosity, honesty, passion, and courage will endure.

As the slow downward spiral continued, the steady flow of friends arriving to be with Shannon was overwhelming. Charmian and Renie often came by, and Renie would get in the bed with Shannon and hold her. Tee flew up from the University of Florida for a three hour visit; Catherine, Shannon's yoga teacher, came to anoint her with oil and sing beautiful songs; Disja who had lived in India would stop by each day to deliver Pranic healing; Debbie, another friend, came, and they talked for hours; Sharon and Richard from the church made sure that all of Shannon's flower pots had bright fresh flowers planted; Roberta, Shannon's best friend from school in Mobile, came with her sister Edie; Barbara, Shannon's gynecologist took her for a pedicure; Marla, brought a handmade prayer shawl for comfort, hope, and peace;

and Nancy who knew Ashby from his soccer days, assured Shannon that she would see to it that Hunter and Ashby were given great care. Casseroles and bakery products continued apace.

Hunter had a close friend from the office who was getting married in May at the Grand Hotel in Point Clear, Alabama (close to our hometown of Mobile). Hunter told us that he really wanted to go. As I knew the end was approaching, Shannon and I determined that we should go. I would get a room at the hotel and would invite her family and friends to come visit. She loved that idea. Her women's group, on the other hand, thought it was a terrible idea. As one said, "She does not have the strength to travel." I replied that Shannon and her family were thrilled about their chance to see each other and, no matter what, we were making the trip. I rented a Suburban and arranged to have a nurse accompany us. We rolled out of Atlanta with Shannon sitting comfortably in the front seat, supported by pillows and covered with blankets. I could tell she was very happy to be going. We arrived at the hotel and got Shannon into the wheelchair I had ordered. Our room was right off the lobby, adjacent to the day room and bar. Her sister Katie arrived soon after we did. Hugs and tears began.

The next morning, the nurse and I got Shannon up. She exhibited amazing energy as we rolled her into the day room. It was not long before family members and friends arrived. In spite of the situation, joy was in the room. Ann, her lifelong friend and one of the bridesmaids in our wedding joined us. She handed Shannon a brown bag. Before she even opened it, Shannon asked, "Is this a bag of cherries?" Ann smiled and shouted a loud, "Yes." They told me the story of when they were young girls, they often went out into the Gulf on Ann's father's boat. During these trips, they would sit on the stern, eat the cherries, and "spit the pits." Many other stories with loving friends and family filled the room that day, and, despite her weakness, Shannon did not want to leave the day room to rest until later in the afternoon.

After a short nap, it was time to go to the wedding reception for Hunter's friends, Adam and Barclay. Shannon was reluctant to go, "There won't be anyone there that I know except Adam." I asked if she would let me roll her there for a brief time since it was in the hotel. She hesitantly agreed. As we arrived in the ballroom, I overheard someone say, "That's Shannon Miller, isn't it?" Before I could get her across the room, seven or eight chairs surrounded her with friends from high school and her old neighborhood. A lively conversation continued for almost two hours. When I told her, "Shannon, we have to get you to bed," she gave me one of those looks of, "Are you telling me what to do?" She finally agreed and we slowly wound down a joyful evening.

May 12th was Mother's Day. All the family who lived in the area gathered in our room to celebrate with Shannon. There were balloons, flowers, and lots of cards. We talked, and again Shannon expressed great joy to be around people she loved. Soon, it was time to load the car and travel home.

Instead of taking the shortest route back to Atlanta, I suggested we return by going across the bay and driving through our old Mobile neighborhoods. On the way, she said, "I would like to get an oyster loaf at Wintzell's." This was one of our favorite Mobile rituals. We stopped. I ran inside to get our dinners, and, even though Shannon no longer had an appetite for much of anything, she ate six oysters, savoring each one with delight.

The following week, my first cousins, John and his wife Susan, Fred and his wife Patty, and David traveled to Atlanta for our annual reunion. This year, as always, we shared family stories and updates about our lives. But the sadness of the situation overshadowed the normality of the reunion. From a rented house nearby, the cousins and spouses would come to visit late each afternoon and help with the dinner. It turned into a family support group until the end.

During dinner the first night of their visit, David posed a question, "Shannon, is there anything we can do to make your life more complete?"

Shannon replied, "I would like to have my book finished and published." For the past several years, Shannon had been working on her memoir about our struggles to learn what was wrong with our sons; the challenges of living with DM; and her role raising awareness, fundraising, and advocating for families affected by DM. It weighed heavily on Shannon that she had not yet found a publisher, and she was disappointed that her story would not be told in the way that she had hoped.

Patty, Fred's wife, who is also a writer and teacher, volunteered to help me complete Shannon's book. To do justice to editing the manuscript, Patty wanted to learn more about what Shannon hoped to accomplish with the book. The next night after dinner, Patty sat with Shannon and me and recorded over two hours of detailed information about Shannon's experiences described in the book and her hopes for future DM research and treatment. Shannon was exhausted at the end of the session but encouraged that Patty and I would see to it that her book would get published.

On June 3rd, the Crossroads nurse told me she thought Shannon had only hours to live. I sat with her telling stories of our lives together. I slept next to her in the bed, holding her through the night. The next morning, the Crossroads nurse was amazed at Shannon's perseverance.

Mid-morning of June 4th, Liz, the priest from St. Luke's, our Episcopal Church we had attended since the early 1970s, came by to administer the Last Rites. My brother Wayne and I stood with the priest by Shannon's bed as she read. Wayne and I responded to the readings. And finally, the prayer, "As you are outwardly anointed with this oil, so may our heavenly Father grant you the inward anointing of the Holy Spirit. Of his great mercy, may he forgive you your sins, release you from suffering, and restore you to wholeness and strength. May he deliver you from all evil, preserve you in all goodness, and bring you to everlasting life; through Jesus Christ our Lord. Amen."

When Liz got to the "through Jesus Christ our Lord", Shannon began to kick her feet, indicating her displeasure. Shannon believed wholeheartedly in Jesus Christ's teachings as a way of life but did not believe she had to go through Jesus to have a relationship with God. Liz recognized her message from earlier discussions with Shannon and stopped. Shannon may have been near death, but she was clear about her views and determined to express them to the end.

I came and went from the room as family and a limited number of friends sat by Shannon's bed. In mid-afternoon, Hunter was sitting by his mother, holding her hand. At four o'clock,

Hunter came out of the room shouting for me to come. Shannon had died peacefully with Hunter holding her hand.

***

Life without Shannon was more difficult than I had expected. Sadness prevailed and will never completely dissipate. The most challenging part is that Shannon and I were inextricably linked for nearly 43 years. Together we were the fabric of the Lord family as we supported each other in life's joys and challenges, both routine and complex. Now, as I look around, there is no Shannon, but her memory will linger forever.

Throughout this ordeal, I have been supported by a host of family and friends. Everywhere I go I got many hugs and offers to help. And, as Shannon would expect, I got busy responding to the estate matters, medical / insurance challenges, and writing thank you notes to those who had been so generous with their love and compassion. I also began to resume my work with my consulting business. Hunter and Ashby became my priority as a single parent. In the four years since Shannon died, Hunter, Ashby, and I have adjusted to life diminished by the loss of Shannon. Hunter continues to work at Camp Twin Lakes and remains optimistic and friendly, but sadly, his stamina and physical capabilities are slowly declining. Ashby still struggles with life in general, and drugs in particular. He struggles to work part time for me doing administrative work for my consulting firm. As I move forward with life, I have dedicated myself to caring for them in a way that Shannon would expect.

Shannon responded to many life challenges but always moved through them with joy and exhilaration with the help of her creative process, close human connections, compassion, determination, therapy, and her belief in the ability to "choose one's attitude in a given set of circumstances ... the last of the human freedoms," as described by Victor Frankl in Man's Search for Meaning.

I remember Shannon with the words spoken by a guest at Babette's Feast by Isak Dinesen, a novel we both admired: "In our human foolishness and short-sightedness, we imagine that grace is finite. But the moment comes when our eyes are opened and we realize that grace is infinite. Grace, my friends, demands nothing of us but that we shall await it with confidence and acknowledge it in gratitude.... Grace takes us all to its bosom and declares general amnesty."

Shannon loved Hunter, Ashby, and me unconditionally, as she did all her family and friends. With the grace of an angel, she would leave us with the admonition: "cherish your relationships."

Post Script

Jonathan Ashby Lord, 35, died at home in Atlanta April 9, 2017, after a long struggle with myotonic dystrophy and drug addiction. Born in Atlanta July 18, 1981, Ashby was the son of Larry Lord and the late Shannon Miller Lord and the stepson of Peggy Walton-Walker Lord (Peggy and Larry, friends from 1965, married June 2016).

Ashby graduated from The Galloway School, Class of 2000, in Atlanta where the arts faculty recognized his exceptional creativity in ceramics and painting. Ashby also excelled in soccer, playing both for Galloway and Concorde Fire Soccer Club in a highly competitive environment. He was co-captain of the Galloway team his senior year and he was selected All-State. Ashby's club played at the highest level of youth soccer, twice travelling to compete with local and professional youth teams in England.

Despite Ashby's valiant struggle to overcome his drug addiction, the scourge of myotonic dystrophy coupled with his addiction became a barrier to his creativity and athleticism. Fortunately, it never interfered with Ashby's love of animals—for which he had a special magnetism—or his particular talent for making friends with a wide variety of people.

Absorbed in the St. Luke's Episcopal memorial service for Ashby, listening to the poignant homily, my eyes were drawn to the Good Shepherd mural on the chancel wall. I became focused on the lamb around the neck of the shepherd who was lost but now found. It reminded me of the vulnerability and wounded life of Ashby. I then remembered a question I asked Hunter the night after Ashby's death, "What one thing would you say about Ashby?" His powerful answer was: "He loved protecting me." Amidst all the turmoil of Ashby's life, with Hunter's words I understood that Ashby, who needed so much protection, could also himself be the protector.

Ashby had recently entered another rehabilitation program, this time at the Bluff Plantation, an intensive inpatient facility in Augusta, Georgia, where he had experienced amazing success. The Bluff was followed by a sober living facility in Augusta and another in Atlanta. He had such good results that he felt he wanted to return home again, excited to be once again part of the family.

Early April, he went to the emergency room experiencing a sensation of insects crawling over his skin. I later learned it is called formication and is a common side effect of cocaine, Ritalin, Wellbutrin, and other drugs. He had picked and scratch himself causing self-induced bleeding and excoriations on his legs where he thought he saw his moles were moving. My heart sank. I knew he had returned to using.

On the night of April 3rd, Peggy, Hunter and I went to dinner at the boy's favorite restaurant where we had an amazingly happy time together. We were so excited that Ashby was back to being his wonderful self. When we returned home, he said he had met a girl and was going to see her. We discouraged him going but he went anyway. He returned home about 3:42 am and went to his room. Around 2:00 pm on Sunday, Peggy went to his room to get him up to come eat. She found him not breathing, called out to me, started CPR and I called 911. Peggy continued to give CPR. The Fire Rescue and EMTs arrived quickly. He could not be resuscitated.

The autopsy report read:

It is my opinion that Jonathan Lord died of the combined toxic effects of morphine, codeine and cocaine. The combination of morphine and codeine suggests heroin use. Morphine is a drug produced from the metabolism of many opiate compounds including heroin. It depresses the central nervous system and can be fatal by causing respiratory depression. Fatality rates are higher in patients who use other drugs such as benzodiazepines and / or cocaine. Codeine is an opioid and can be found as a contaminant in heroin. In high levels, it can depress the central nervous system causing respiratory depression, coma or death. In addition to cocaine, benzoylecgonine (an inactive cocaine metabolite), was identified in Mr. Lord's blood sample. Cocaine causes coronary artery spasms in addition to increases in blood pressure resulting in the development of dysrhythmias (abnormal heart rhythms). Prolonged dysrhythmias may cause an individual's death as the blood does not circulate in an efficient manner to the body's internal organs including the brain.

Opioids and benzodiazepines are two of the greatest hazards for someone with myotonic dystrophy. Even though Ashby knew of their potential for death, he could not control the need to use. Through the years, I would refer to his drug use as "the beast". In the end, it was the power of "the beast" that, while he valiantly struggled to defeat it, Ashby could not overcome.

Epilogue by Tetsuo (Tee) Ashizawa, MD

One early summer morning of year 2000, I arrived at my office at the Baylor College of Medicine and turned on my desktop computer. Checking emails as my first daily routine, I found several in my inbox. I noticed one from smlord@mindspring.com. I had never seen this address and, after a brief hesitation, I opened it. It was from Shannon. Of course, I did not know her then. She wrote that she had raised some money at a family event to support research on myotonic dystrophy because her two sons suffered from the disease. She further stated that this was the first time she had done fundraising, and asked what she should do with the donation. Having previously consulted with her husband Larry, she sent emails to myotonic dystrophy researchers, but no one responded.

Finally, Shannon contacted Professor Peter Harper, one of the most respected medical geneticists in the field and the sole author of a famous monograph "Myotonic Dystrophy." Dr. Harper kindly recommended me to Shannon. The connection was made, and the Hunter Research Fund was established at Baylor College of Medicine where I was a faculty member.

In December of that year, the annual meeting of the American Society of Human Genetics (ASHG) was being held in Philadelphia. Shannon asked me if she and her family might be able to meet some of the myotonic dystrophy researchers. It was short notice, but I organized a small meeting of investigators in a hotel one evening. I waited anxiously for Shannon and her family's arrival. Then, I saw a tall impeccably dressed couple walking toward me with beautiful smiles on their faces. They were accompanied by their two sons, Hunter and Ashby, who were in their twenties.

The meeting went on with scientific presentations of the latest data and good discussions. At the end and before dinner, Shannon introduced herself and her family. As Shannon had predicted, most scientists had never seen persons with the disease which they had been studying. Conversations with her and her sons made a huge impression on the researchers' minds that night. In her short speech, Shannon's intelligence, sincerity, and will to fight the disease struck everyone. Her love and care for her sons was emotionally reflected among her words, along with frustration and despair as a mother. I witnessed that she re-vitalized the commitment and determination of these researchers in pursuit of their missions. That same night I was presented a check for $155,000 to further our research.

After that meeting, I asked Shannon if she would come to Houston to further discuss her work and her expectations about the use of the funds she had raised with some of my colleagues and me. During that discussion, I brought up the idea that she might want to address her view of the disease at the next International Myotonic Dystrophy Consortium (IDMC-3) meeting in Kyoto which was scheduled in the fall of 2001. She was uncertain, but I knew she would make a significant impact. She accepted and as I predicted, Shannon gave an articulate and compassionate speech. And, with that speech, she became a star spokesperson for patients and families living with the disease. With recommendations from IDMC investigators, invitations from the National Institutes of Health (NIH), the Center for Disease Control (CDC), and other government and private organizations were extended to Shannon to speak in their meetings as a patient advocate. Shannon also contacted support groups for myotonic dystrophy including the Myotonic Dystrophy Assistance and Awareness Support Group (MDAASG) in Los Angeles, California.

At IDMC-3 in Glasgow, Scotland in 2003, Shannon met Margaret Bowler, the founder of the Myotonic Dystrophy Support Group (MDSG) in the UK. Margaret had been working closely with Professor Harper and other UK physicians and researchers. At the IDMC-4 in Quebec City, Canada, organizers and Margaret invited many myotonic dystrophy patients to the banquet where they sat with physicians and scientists. The MDSG was (and still is) a patient-centric support organization. It later became an important model in founding the Myotonic Dystrophy Foundation (MDF). Shannon became the inaugural Chairperson of the MDF in 2006, which is now the world's largest patient organization focused solely on myotonic dystrophy (see www.myotonic.org).

The trip to Glasgow also offered great personal satisfaction to Shannon. Her Hunter ancestors came from Glasgow, and the Hunterian Museum is located on the University of Glasgow campus. This museum has an impressive collection of articles that

John and William Hunter, part of Shannon's Hunter Clan, left to the University in the 18th century. For those who are interested in history of medicine, I recommend a book entitled "Knife Man" written by Wendy Moore. This book is a biography of John Hunter who established modern surgery based on human anatomy (cadaver dissections) and physiology (therapeutic experimentations). He was a genius and, had he lived ten more years, he could have introduced his version of evolution theory before Charles Darwin. His brother, William Hunter, is an equally famous figure and regarded as the father of modern obstetrics. The Hunter Research Fund was named after Shannon's son, Hunter and her ancestral roots.

Larry's Last Chapter is a powerful testimony of Shannon's character that readers might have noted while reading earlier chapters. Larry told me that it was extremely difficult for him to add this Last Chapter of her life. She died from malignant mixed Mullerian tumor (MMMT), also known as Uterine Carcinosarcoma. While she was only mildly affected by myotonic dystrophy, the risk for developing female organ cancers is up to 7.6 times higher in patients with myotonic dystrophy (regardless of the severity of their myotonic dystrophy) than normal individuals. MMMT is an extremely aggressive cancer, and my heart sank when I heard the bad news that she was diagnosed with it. Larry vividly described how she found and fought the tumors. He describes not only how she died, but also how she lived.

Death is a difficult fact to accept for anyone, but we all will have to face it someday. Shannon lived and died courageously, accepting her fate, taking her own initiative to deal with it, cherishing the love that she gave and received, and keeping her dignity, no matter what. Larry described the moment when she signed the agreement for palliative care — "*Shannon had no hesitation. We began the journey of Shannon dying.*" I thought it was very Shannon. However, Shannon was by no means an iron woman. When I visited during her palliative care at home, she told me how scared she was and how much she worried about her sons.

She was fighting a tremendous emotional turmoil with indescribable feelings of sadness, helplessness, hopelessness, fear, anger, frustration, and guilt, all storming over her confidence and will. She was a saddened, emotionally fragile, and physically weak lady who frequently broke into tears. She repeatedly told me that she did not want to die. She was a very sensitive person showing all the vulnerability that a human being can have. Yet, she had already planned how everything should proceed in the worst circumstances in her life. Her inquiries about how to best secure her tissues for research — both from her original surgery and from her autopsy — are clear examples of her courageous and noble response to her illness and inevitable death. It was her expression of dignity.

In her palliative care bed, I could still see the same Shannon whom I saw the very first time in Philadelphia — a tall impeccably dressed lady with her aura of dignity. She was a great friend. I miss her. Her memory still lives in my heart. Her tissues and cells are safely stored at the University of Florida and used for research. Her thoughts and heart are preserved in this book. I hope patients, families, healthcare professionals, scientists, policy makers, and totally unrelated people will read this book and share her story.

—Tetsuo (Tee) Ashizawa, M.D.

Epilogue by Patty Ramsey, 2016

On June 4, 2013, Shannon Lord died of cancer. The grace and dignity that she brought to this final phase of her journey embodied the vulnerability, insights, and strength that shine through this book.

Larry is my husband's cousin, and, over the years at many family gatherings, I got to know Shannon well. Like many people in Shannon's life, I benefitted enormously from her wisdom and compassion. Although my family and I are not affected by myotonic dystrophy, our children have faced many challenges as transracial and international adoptees. At family gatherings, I often poured out my heartbreak about our latest crises to Shannon. She was a wonderful listener, and she taught me how to "ride the wave of sadness" as she herself had so often done. Her move from depression to activism inspired me. I shifted my own research to studying the psychological aspects of adoption to better understand and support my own family and others coping with the complexities of adoption and foster care. I call it "putting pain to work."

I had the privilege of being with Shannon the week before she died. During that time, we talked about this book and how much she wanted to have it published. Although she was sad, exhausted, and in pain, she spoke passionately about her desire to make this final contribution to people affected by myotonic dystrophy and to others going through their own life challenges. She eagerly accepted my offer to edit the book and work with Larry to bring it to publication.

Spending that week with Shannon in her home was a life-changing gift. Surrounded by her beautiful artwork and "arrangements" that somehow express both order and spontaneity, we talked about her life and her legacy. I came to understand the meaning of a life well lived in a whole new way and witnessed the power of acceptance and transformation. She exemplified the Frankl quote she included in her book and that quote ironically turned out to be prescient: "When we are no longer able to change a situation — just think of an incurable disease such as inoperable cancer, we are challenged to change ourselves." (Frankl, p. 116).

As I have edited this book, I have tried to "channel" Shannon, to bring her life and words to light as best as I can. Throughout the process, I have felt that I have accompanied her through the many odysseys of her life — feeling her frustration, sadness, determination, and joy. During this time, I also have become a frequent "visitor" on the MDF website and have seen how many families are finding support, hope, and practical advice, as well as learning about recent research and treatment options. It is truly a wonderful community and an inspiring legacy of Shannon's efforts to reach out and bring people together. I am profoundly grateful to have been a part of Shannon's life.

Thus, I salute you, Shannon—you are a beautiful soul and intrepid warrior. Even though our earthly paths have diverged, I know that we will always be true companions in mind and spirit.

Addendum by Peggy Walton-Walker Lord, 2017

*Shannon Miller Lord was an extraordinary woman, an inspi-*rational person. Of that fact, I am quite clear despite having never met her on this mortal plane, except through her family, friends, and most importantly, the gift of her book. Therefore, in the spirit of life continuing after death, I add my own thoughts.

Shannon's husband, Larry Lord, now my husband, re-entered my life six months after Shannon's death, forty-seven years after he and I first met, and 17 years after my husband, Keith Walker, died from cancer. I had felt then that the spirits of Shannon and Keith, with the encouragement of our mothers, had brought us back together.

Larry and I first met in Mobile, Alabama where we both grew up. His brother, Wayne, introduced us shortly before my last year at Birmingham Southern College and Larry's at Georgia Tech.

We dated briefly in Mobile and a few more times when I was in graduate school in New York City at Union Theological Seminary and Larry was in the Navy stationed in Rhode Island. He traveled to New York where we shared dinners. But those times were short lived when I got a Hollywood movie contract which took me to Los Angeles. Larry was shipped out to Vietnam. We both enjoyed full, amazing lives with wonderful spouses and creative careers.

Larry came back into my life after hearing my brother-in-law, Charlie Monk on SiriusXM radio and tracking me down in New Orleans. He told stories of his life with Shannon and his two sons but also shared the difficulties that had come with myotonic dystrophy.

Shannon's huge family and giant circle of friends have embraced me, generously sharing experiences of her and her sons, Hunter and Ashby. My first meeting with Hunter convinced me to believe that it would be a challenge to connect with him. He didn't want me in his dad's life. He felt that he and Larry were doing quite well as they were. Ashby, on the other hand, embraced me with heart-felt joy. He was my advocate. And soon, as Hunter got to know me better and learned that I was going to love him and Ashby as well as his father, that relationship began to blossom and continues to deepen every day.

I soon learned that Ashby was battling not only the war of myotonic dystrophy but also a wrath of opiate and drug-related demons. Unfortunately, that war turned out to be too challenging to overcome. Ashby's tragic death saddened us all. I feel that his mother, knowing he was continuing to repeatedly struggle in this life, decided to call him to join her. Hunter has an amazing ability to deal with his disability and I admire him.

We all experienced a kind of happy ending with Ashby. He had successfully gone through yet another rehab, this time at the Bluff Plantation in Augusta. After the most successful of his rehab experiences, he continued in a halfway-house and was going to therapy. Six months later, he felt he was ready to move back home.

Ashby walked in and appeared to be the happiest and most handsome I had ever seen him. The family—Larry, Hunter, Ashby and I—had a joyous last supper at his favorite taco restaurant. The next day, I found him on his bed. He was not breathing. I tried CPR until the paramedics arrived. I continue to be humbly thankful that Ashby was in my life for three, too brief years.

Shannon's memoir is a gift for which I shall be forever grateful. She introduced herself to me through her own precious words, sharing a bit of her life—before and with Larry—and what she had been through in her pursuit of unraveling the mysteries of myotonic dystrophy. I am blessed to have read her book. I believe everyone will benefit from reading it.

Acknowledgements from Shannon Miller Lord

For...

...family and friends, a very, very long list, with whom I journeyed through life: each one I LOVE...

... the people whom I met in my travels through many parts of the world over the decades to be able to engage societies and cultures where I learned to love and to serve...

... my Jewish Group who would listen with intensity and unconditional love even though I may have told the story many times before...

... my writing group and my teacher who, through their constructive criticism and encouragement, showed me the path to writing...

... all the dedicated physicians, researchers and volunteers: Nick Kraweiecki, MD; Tee Ashizawa, MD; Charles Thornton, MD; Sir Peter Harper, CBE; Richard Moxley, M; John Day, MD, PhD; Tom Cooper, MD; Richard Lymn, PhD; Darren Monckton, PhD; Laura Ranum, PhD; Maury Swanson, PhD; Geneviève Gourdon. PhD; Giovanni Meola, MD; Mário

Gomes-Pereira, PhD; Margaret Bowler; Alice Gunderson; Jeremy Kelly; John Brekka; Barry Wald; and, Lisa Harvey-Duren who gave me incredible encouragement and support...

... the employees of Lord, Aeck & Sargent and Camp Twin Lakes who were Hunter's community of friendship and support...

... the engaging stories from writers I have read, stimulating thoughts which let me grow my voice and come to life in my own story...

... my first editor: Michael Ames at Vanderbilt Press ...

... family insight from Susan Tucker, a treasured cousin and archivist; Buck St. John, my aunt who could convey family history for hours; Shannon Hunter and Howard Barney, who sought out and compiled information for our reunion...

Acknowledgements from Larry Lord

For...

...Patricia Ramsey who diligently worked with me over the course of three years to finalize Shannon's memoir...

... Peggy Walton-Walker Lord and Cynthia Whitcomb who lovingly edited the manuscript...

... Bob Babcock, publisher, Jan Babcock, marketing consultant, and Mark Babcock, creative consultant, at Deeds Publishing...

... Hunter who continues to live a life of "whatever" ...

Appendix

The following reflections written by Shannon before she became ill reflect her hopes for how she and this book might contribute to research, diagnosis, management, and treatment related to DM. They also demonstrate her relentless curiosity and determination to learn as much as she could and to pass it on to others. We encourage readers to follow her footsteps—read her words, follow up on the references she cites, and share new hope for the future with others.

Even as I immersed myself in the field of DM research, questions—some old and abiding and others new and intriguing—clamored in my head.

Is myotonic dystrophy best described as a neuromuscular disease?

Would it be better to call it a multi-systemic disease instead?

Is it a neurological disease?

A cardiac disease?

Narcolepsy?

An anxiety disorder?

A gastrointestinal disease?

A personality disorder?

A mental disorder?

Early in my nearly 30-year odyssey with myotonic dystrophy, I was confounded not only by the odd assortment of symptoms confronting us but also ones that I learned about from other people, ones that we had not yet encountered. The disease seemed to transcend all logic. Our family journey began with the perplexing childhood form that affected the central nervous system and eluded diagnosis for seven years. Gradually it morphed into adult symptoms affecting the muscular systems. The more families I met made me realize I was not alone in my bewilderment.

For over a dozen years now, I've been watching at close range a stalwart group of translational and clinical scientists working tirelessly to explain the confounding variability of myotonic dystrophy. They are focused on unraveling the molecular mysteries that cause our family disease, providing effective clinical management, and developing viable treatments to reverse the symptoms.

I now know that overwhelming numbers of physicians are ill-prepared to diagnose and understand the intricate aspects of this rare disease and many other rare diseases. At the meeting in Kyoto, Dr. Bruno Eymard, a French neurologist, validated my years of frustration when he reported his study showing that fifty-one out of eighty-five DM patients with at least two significant presenting symptoms had been misdiagnosed for six to thirteen years by general physicians, ophthalmologists, pediatricians, endocrinologists, cardiologists, neurologists, and at least six other specialists.

Part of the confusion about DM lies in its rarity and inconsistencies. First, it affects one in 8,000 people worldwide. Because of these low numbers, it is often called an "orphan disease" along with thousands of others. Thus, in fairness to doctors, some never encounter a single patient with DM during their lifetime of practice. Second, there are numerous possible symptoms that may—or may not—emerge; they can vary in age of onset and severity within the same family, even among siblings. Dr. Harper, in the handbook he wrote for families, said, "[Myotonic dystrophy] is probably the most variable disorder known in medicine, something that causes difficulties to doctors in recognizing it, as well as to patients and their families" (p. 4)

Doctors, even when they know someone has DM, may not recognize the effects and take them into account. For the last few years at my annual physical, our dedicated family internist has said to me, "Fifty-two beats per minute. Good. You've got a runner's heart!" And each time I reply, "But I'm not a runner, remember? My heart has gradually slowed down, most probably because of myotonic dystrophy." Perhaps having a runner's heart is a healthy, logical thing—if you're a runner. But how low should the heart rate be allowed to go before preemptive measures are taken, like implanting a cardiac device?

Then there are those with DM who have annual physicals with normal EKG's and feel confident they're in good health. Three months later, with no warning, they have a severe cardiac event and may suddenly die.

Standard tests often fail to ask the right questions to identify problems and reveal how a person actually functions. Hunter, with high IQ scores, has uttered on several occasions, "I have all this information in my head, but it doesn't do me any good." Furthermore, appropriate tests are not always administered. What doctor routinely checks for tumors on the parotid gland? Where are the gastroenterologists who understand how the tongue and esophagus are affected by the disease where the gastrointestinal tract is slow and uncoordinated in its movement of food? How many of them consider DM's bacterial overgrowth that produces gas as one possible explanation of abdominal pain?

Where are the experts who understand the impact of the gene defect on the endocrine system? Could it contribute to excessive daytime sleepiness? And what about infertility issues? Are doctors aware of the possible correlation between DM and insulin resistance and diabetes?

What about people who do not know they have this disorder—or even some who do—and are anesthetized for routine gall bladder surgery and end up in ICU for six weeks or die of cardiorespiratory failure during the post-operative period because the doctor does not know of the risks with anesthesia in this population? How can bad outcomes be avoided?

Better education of doctors in many specialties and shared information among attending team members across specialty lines are desperately needed. Some DM patients find that neuromuscular experts have a primary interest in a single muscle disease, like ALS or Duchenne. They become discouraged and conclude that "[The doctor] wasn't interested in me at all. I don't want to go back to him. Does anyone know of a doctor in this area who knows about *my* disease?" Many DM patients do not see themselves as having *muscular dystrophy*. They know that the challenges and treatment for Duchenne are vastly different from those of DM. Furthermore, they realize that treatment needs vary even within congenital, juvenile-onset, and adult-onset patients.

Diagnosing children can be extremely tricky, as the stories of Hunter and Ashby reveal, because they are not afflicted with obvious neuromuscular symptoms that are characteristic of adult-onset DM. Instead, as Anne-Berit Ekstrom (2009) found:

"...In everyday life, it appears that [children] with DM1 primarily are affected by central nervous system-related symptoms such as cognitive deficits and neuropsychiatric problems, rather than by their neuromuscular systems."

As a result, DM symptoms in children may be confused with a wide array of cognitive and emotional disabilities including mental retardation, learning disabilities, ADHD, Asperger's Syndrome, autism spectrum, schizophrenia, anxiety, personality disorders, and obsessive-compulsive tendencies. Alternatively, does DM trigger full-blown mental disorders? Was the psychiatrist correct in her diagnosis of childhood schizophrenia in Hunter?

As I learned about the disparate symptoms and timing of this disease, our own lives and history began to make more sense. We spent all those years and dollars trying to find the best educational settings for Hunter and Ashby, trying to understand and explain their challenges to teachers, coaches, and counselors. To spare future generations of DM families, we desperately need to understand how this disease affects brain development and to disseminate this information to pediatricians, psychologists, neuropsychologists, pediatric neurologists, and educators.

These concerns inevitably raise the question about genetic testing of children. Currently many geneticists discourage parents from testing asymptomatic children until they can make their own decision at age 18. However, one cannot declare that the child is asymptomatic without a consistent and comprehensive profile of affected individuals and possible symptoms, beginning with the impact on the brain. Without this knowledge of the disease and astute observations, doctors will continue to under-diagnose and therefore underserve children and their families, leaving them to embark on unnecessary long and frustrating odysseys to find the causes of perplexing behaviors.

Further complicating this disease is the phenomenon of *anticipation*, which means that, as the gene passes to offspring, the genetic mutation usually enlarges, and the symptoms become more severe and appear at an earlier age. However, there is no way to predict the severity or even type of symptoms that may eventually appear. It's a little like being trapped in the middle of guerrilla warfare and having no idea from which direction the next assault will come.

The disease is extraordinarily complex. Not only does it change across generations, it also varies within the same individual and across time. Because of *somatic mosaicism*, the size of the mutations can differ in the blood and various organs and systems within the same person as well as within different cells in the same organ. And the mutations often enlarge as an individual ages.

More and more symptoms are being identified all the time. When Hunter had a grand mal seizure in his early twenties, his MRI revealed white lesions randomly scattered in his brain that resembled those found in patients with multiple sclerosis. His epileptologist was afraid Hunter had MS in addition to DM and ordered a spinal tap. Hunter did not have multiple sclerosis. A couple of years later, I read that white lesions had been found in the brains of some DM patients, and I mailed the doctor a copy of the article. These different kinds and numbers of anomalies scattered in the brain — sort of like buck-shot — can cause a cluster of symptoms that can vary from person to person — depending on their number and location.

Some of the behaviors resulting from central nervous system involvement have been described in DM literature as problems with *executive function*. I first sat up and took notice while reading an article, "The Brain and MMD" (Myotonic Muscular Dystrophy), in the September-October 2008 MDA *Quest Magazine*. There, Dr. Patricia Evans, a pediatric neurologist at Children's Medical Center in Dallas, listed challenges she has identified in children with DM through neuropsychological testing. They include impaired visual-spatial memory (needed to communicate nonverbally, to read faces, and to figure out where your body is in space, as well as to locate people and objects around you); verbal abstract reasoning impairment; and attention disorders. She noted that, although children with DM often are diagnosed with ADHD, perhaps instead they have deficits in *executive function* (EF) located in the pre-frontal cortex.

Executive function is described by Evans and others as a spectrum that involves drive, motivation, decision making, focusing, inhibition, planning, and the ability to suppress short-term gains for long-term goals. These functions are housed in the pre-frontal cortex. Dr. Thomas E. Brown at Yale University School of Medicine described EF using the following metaphor:

One way of thinking about Executive Function is to picture a symphony orchestra whose members are all very fine musicians. Even when the musicians are excellent, if there is not a conductor to organize and integrate efforts of the individual musicians, getting them to play their respective parts in the same piece at the same time—one who can bring in the strings, and the tympani, etc. and then fade them out at the proper moment—the music will not be very good…The difficulties originate in the management system that controls and manages these activities, integrating them moment by moment for managing the multiple tasks of daily life.

Coupled with executive function deficits, Dr. Evans mentions a high incidence of mood disorders, specifically anxiety and depression, in children with DM. These latter disorders are aggravated by the weak muscles around the mouth and tongue that make it difficult for some individuals with DM to show facial expressions or to speak clearly.

Because our experience fit so closely with her research findings, I wrote to Dr. Evans. She wrote back to me in an e-mail, *Although I was not taught to do this in residency, when I now receive a new referral for cognitive difficulties, I always test these children for muscle diseases in addition to neuropsychological evaluations.* Her actions illustrate how well research and patient and family advocacy can benefit practice.

Consistent with Dr. Evans' conclusions about impairment of executive functioning, DM researchers are finding that the most affected part of the brain appears to be the frontal cortex that governs motivation, thinking, weighing risks and benefits, and making decisions that together make up the executive function. These dysfunctions may in turn be related to drug use. According to Dr. Nora Volkow, Director of the National Institute on Drug

Abuse (NIDA) at NIH, the frontal cortex also is involved in addiction. She asks, "Does a dysfunction in decision making [taking place in the frontal cortex] predispose one person to drug use, while in another person does drug use trigger such a dysfunction [in the prefrontal cortex]?" Dr. Volkow also mentions that there are "decision-making disorders" characterized by disruption of the frontal brain's capacity for reason and control. Perhaps my question to the counselor at Ashby's first drug rehab center as to whether myotonic dystrophy played any part in Ashby's addiction was not as absurd as he thought it was.

The toll that these brain disorders take was illustrated in a recent email from an advocate and devoted mother of a twenty-year old son with DM:

> I fear that ours is still not the disability that will benefit from much that is available. The mental (CNS) aspects of DM are underrated. My son's mood swings and lack of executive decision making skills have me extremely worried. He is bright enough, but DM or depression is stealing his gumption to press on in what we know is a pressure-cooker environment of college.
>
> The world in which this young man dwells differs from my world and his father's. We do not suffer from significant mood swings, inertia, and major executive function deficits. So, what are we parents to do?

Because of these symptoms, people with DM often have difficulty keeping jobs and experience socio-economic deterioration — sometimes abruptly, from one generation to the next. From Dr. Harper's big book, I quote two researchers, Caughey and Myrianthopoulos, as they went about interviewing DM families in England in 1963:

> While in the country in search of a certain myotonic's home, it was often possible to identify a residence by its neglected appearance, the obvious need of repairs, the unkempt yard and garden choked with overgrown grass and weeds, which provided a vivid contrast with the surrounding well-kept homes.

Myotonic dystrophy is truly a family disease; it can be sad and cruel, affecting everyone — those with the mutant gene and those without — the latter often becoming the managers and caregivers for successive generations of affected loved ones. Families yearn desperately for accurate diagnoses and effective treatments.

Although families continue to suffer, investigators are moving closer to potential treatments for DM. Charles Thornton, a neurologist at the University of Rochester, told me not long ago that investigators have made more progress in understanding myotonic dystrophy in the last ten years than in the previous ninety. In 2009, researchers at the University of Rochester Medical Center (URMC) described in the journal *Science* a way to block the genetic flaw at the heart of a common form of muscular dystrophy. The results of the study could pave the way for new therapies that essentially reverse the symptoms of the disease, a way to block the genetic flaw at the heart of a common form of muscular dystrophy. He described how he and his colleagues used a synthetic molecule called an *antisense morpholino oligonucleotide* to reverse DM symptoms in mice and to re-establish the cellular activity that is disrupted by the disease. This success may eventually lead to clinical trials in humans and someday, a therapy or a cure.

When I shared some of this information with Ashby, he said, "I want to be the first person to try the new medicine! I wish this myotonic dystrophy thing had been discovered when I was five; then I might not have done all those awful things I did, and I might have finished college."

I shared Ashby's comments with Dr. Thornton in an email. Despite the tremendous demands on his time, Dr. Thornton took the time to respond and to caution us about false hopes.

...What is 'false hope'? What is the actual cost, in terms of suffering, if things do not go as well as I believe they should?

... But, how to keep [patients] from giving way to disillusionment, if progress is not as fast as people want (and it won't be)..."

POST SCRIPT FROM LARRY

It is now 2017 and the Phase 1/2 of the clinical trials for the use of the drug in humans was conducted in 2015 and 2016. Unfortunately, the drug had limited success when drug levels measured in biopsy tissue from trial participants indicated that the amount of target engagement would not achieve the desired therapeutic benefit to treat the disease. Without the desired drug levels in muscle, based on the valuable data that was gained from the clinical trial, the research and pharmaceutical teams will now pursue the discovery of a more potent drug. We will all be on the tiptoes of expectation and work with those affected with all the love that we can muster as we wait for the success that will someday come.

Contributions

Profits from the sale of this book will be contributed to the Hunter Fund at the Myotonic Dystrophy Foundation.

www.myotonic.org

For those interested in supporting the Myotonic Dystrophy Foundation, contributions can be made to Hunter Fund at myotonic.org or mail to 1004-A O'Reilly Avenue, San Francisco, CA 94129.

Author Shannon Miller Lord

Family Roots: A Mother's Search for Meaning by Marian Shannon Miller Lord is a memoir of a seemingly hopeless revelation of myotonic dystrophy in one of her sons which she traced back to her Hunter roots in Scotland and Ireland. Her long and eventful journey leads her to a life of discovery, reaction and activism.

When Shannon was young, she imagined people who lived charmed lives but she learned this notion to be false. *Family Roots ... A Mother's Search for Meaning* describes her journey from a revelation, to a very dark place, and eventually to freedom, joy and exhilaration overcoming seemingly insurmountable obstacles. She suggests that it is important to tell your story to those who will listen, whether family and friends, therapist, or support group. Over time, if you tell your story enough to those who listen, you will begin to realize that sadness and loss start to diminish. At some point, you realize that you can assume control over your attitude about what has befallen you.

Shannon, a "navy junior", was born in Norfolk, Virginia. With her father in the Navy, as a child, the family moved frequently and forced to adapt to new neighborhoods, new schools, and new friends. But she was fortunate to be born to a mother who adored all five of her children and a father who expected her to do everything her brothers could do, even throw a perfect spiral! As an English major and closet writer for years, along with short stories, journal entries, and other jottings, she squirreled away scratchy notes on yellow pads from parent-teacher conferences, doctors' appointments, report cards, and psychological evaluations to have ready recollection of facts along her life's journey for her memoir.

Shannon attended Bennett College in Millbrook, New York, then returned to Mobile, where she received her Bachelor of Arts degree in English. Later she attended writing courses at Georgia State University.

Printed in the USA
CPSIA information can be obtained
at www.ICGtesting.com
LVHW020302170124
769075LV00018B/73/J

9 781947 309180